Technology Laboratory Guide to Accompany

Calculus with Analytic Geometry

Fifth Edition

Larson/Hostetler/Edwards

David E. Heyd
The Pennsylvania State University
The Behrend College

D. C. Heath and Company
Lexington, Massachusetts   Toronto

Address editorial correspondence to:
D. C. Heath and Company
125 Spring Street
Lexington, MA 02173

Published simultaneously in Canada.

Printed in the United States of America.

International Standard Book Number: 0-669-34943-7

10   9   8   7   6   5   4   3   2   1

Preface

This solutions guide is a supplement to *Calculus with Analytic Geometry, Fifth Edition,* by Roland E. Larson, Robert P. Hostetler, and Bruce H. Edwards. All references to chapters and sections relate to the main text.

To the Student

Continuing innovations in communication and computer technology are causing significant changes in all sectors of our society. These technologies are influencing the way one learns mathematics. The computer/calculator quickly performs time consuming and complex mathematical operations. This allows time to investigate the essential mathematical processes needed to solve problems. Further, the graphics capabilities of these technologies can enhance your problem solving abilities by providing visual representations that lead to insights about mathematical concepts or to problem solutions. This manual has many exercises that use graphics to visualize fundamental concepts in calculus, and the expand the sphere of applications of calculus. Mathematics has always been a supporting discipline for science, engineering and business. Since the computer can quickly process vast quantities of numerical data, the mathematical analysis of this information is now required in an increasing number of academic disciplines.

Wise use of these technologies will enhance one's study of mathematics. However, this use does not guarantee success. The computer and calculator are merely tools. Your ability to effectively use these tools requires that you continually sharpen your problem solving skills and your understanding of fundamental mathematical principles.

Problem Solving Using a Computer/Calculator

Here are some guidelines to consider when using any type of computer/calculator in problem solving.

1. Be sure you understand the operation of your own computer/calculator. You need to be skilled at entering expressions in a way that will guarantee that your computer/calculator is performing the operation correctly.

2. Focus first on analyzing the problem. After you have developed a strategy, you may be able to use your computer/calculator to help implement the strategy. Write down your steps in an organized way to clearly outline the strategy used and the results.

3. Most problems can be solved in a variety of ways. If you choose to solve a problem using a table, try checking the solution with an analytic (or algebraic) approach. If you choose to solve a problem using algebra, try checking the solution with an algebraic approach.

4. After obtaining a solution with a computer/calculator, be sure to ask yourself if the solution is reasonable (within the context of the problem).

5. To lessen the chance of errors, clear the computer/calculator display (and check the settings) before beginning a new problem.

When using a computer/calculator it is important to understand the precision of the results. For instance, what does your utility display when the answer to a problem is 2/3? Some utilities will truncate (drop) the digits which exceed the set number of decimal place accuracy and display 0.6666. Others will round the number and display 0.6667. Although the second display is more accurate, both of these decimal representations of 2/3 contain a rounding error. Some utilities will give the exact answers rather than decimal approximations. Thus, answers involving radicals, trigonometric functions, and logarithmic and exponential functions are left in symbolic (exact) form. Here are some examples.

	Exact	Approximation Rounded To Three Places
a.	$\dfrac{2}{3}$	0.667
b.	$\sqrt{5}$	2.236
c.	$\dfrac{3\pi}{2}$	4.712
d.	$\cos\dfrac{3\pi}{7}$	0.223
e.	$\ln 3$	1.099

To the Instructor

This laboratory manual covers all the major topics in a calculus course. It is designed to use a wide variety of technological tools currently available. Therefore, its emphasis is on calculus and not on the keystrokes for a specific calculator or the capabilities of one software package.

You can adapt the assignments in this manual to best meet the needs of your students. The assignments may be given to an individual student or to a group of students. There are many problems in which students are to use the technology for exploration and then respond to open ended questions. These exercises are particularly useful for small group work in the classroom.

Acknowledgments

The author wishes to acknowledge several people whose help and encouragement were invaluable in the production of this manual. First, I am grateful to Roland E. Larson, Robert P. Hostetler, and Bruce H. Edwards for the privilege of working with them on the main text. I also wish to thank Michele Bliss for typing the manuscript, Jessica Pflueger, Dan Bruce and Greg Janusz for the computer graphics and the staff at D. C. Heath and Company. I am grateful to my wife, Jean, for her love and support during the many months I have worked on this project.

David E. Heyd
The Pennsylvania State University
Erie, Pennsylvania 16563

CONTENTS

This worksheet uses a 2D function grapher with zoom and solve features.

Name _____

Date _____

1. Program a computer/calculator to find the distance between the points $(x_1,\ y_1)$ and $(x_2,\ y_2)$.

In Exercises 2–4, use the program from Exercise 1 to verify that the points are the vertices of the specified polygon. Explain your answer.

2. $(-2,\ 1),\ (3,\ 5),\ (7,\ 0)$

Right triangle

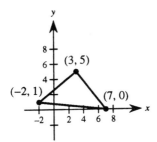

3. $(1, 0),\ (5, 2),\ (6, 5),\ (2, 3)$

Parallelogram

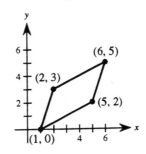

4. $(2,\ -2),\ (1,\ 5),\ (5,\ 2)$

Isosceles triangle

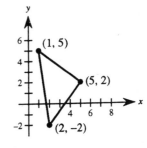

5. Use a computer/calculator to graph a circle of radius 3 with the given center. (It may be necessary to graph the circle as two semicircles.)

a. $(h,\ k) = (0,\ 0)$

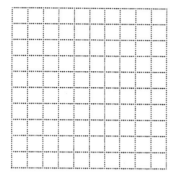

b. $(h,\ k) = (3,\ 0)$

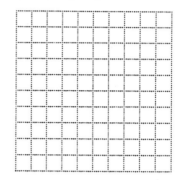

c. $(h,\ k) = (-4,\ 2)$

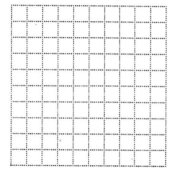

d. $(h,\ k) = (0,\ -3)$

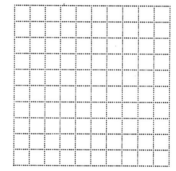

6. a. Use a computer/calculator to graph each circle.

$$\left(x - \tfrac{1}{2}\right)^2 + (y + 4)^2 = 16$$
$$(x - 2)^2 + (y + 4)^2 = 1$$
$$(x - 2)^2 + (y + 4)^2 = \tfrac{25}{4}$$
$$(x - 2)^2 + (y + 4)^2 = 25$$

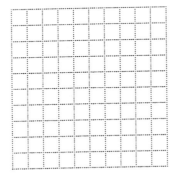

b. Compare the graphs of the <u>last three</u> equations. What are the circles of such a family called?

c. Use the zoom feature of a computer/calculator to approximate the coordinates of any points of intersection of the circles.

d. Use the solve feature of a computer/calculator to find the exact* coordinates of the points of intersection.

* See the illustrations of exact real numbers in the Preface.

This worksheet uses a 2D function grapher with zoom and solve features.

Name _____

Date _____

In Exercises 1–4, use a computer/calculator. a. Graph the equation. b. Use the zoom feature to approximate any x-intercepts. c. Use the solve feature to find the exact x-intercepts.

1. $y = 3x^3 + 6x^2 - 2x - 4$

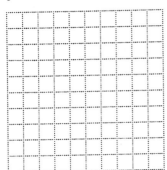

2. $y = |x^2 + 2x - 3|$

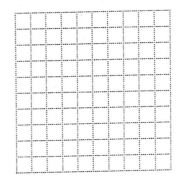

3. $y = 5x\sqrt{100 - x^2}$

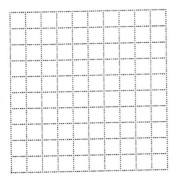

4. $3x^2 - 4y^2 = 8$

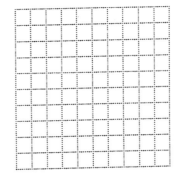

5. Even with a computer/calculator, it may be difficult to find the x-intercepts of an equation. Consider the equation $y = 5x^5 - 3x^4 - 2180x^3 + 1308x^2 + 72{,}000x - 43{,}200$.

    a. Use the zoom feature to approximate the x-intercepts of the graph accurate to three decimal places.

    b. This particular polynomial has rational zeros. Find them and use the results to factor the polynomial.

6. Find an equation of the form $y = a_n x^n + a_{n-1} x^{n-1} + \cdots + a_1 x + a_0$ having the following characteristics and sketch its graph. If this is not possible, give a reason.

    a. A second degree polynomial equation with no x-intercept and one y-intercept

    b. A third degree polynomial with no x-intercept

    c. A fourth degree polynomial with 4 x-intercepts

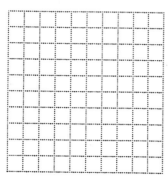
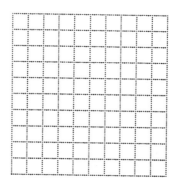
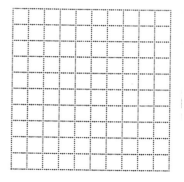

7. Find a possible polynomial equation for each of the following graphs.

a.

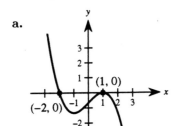

b.

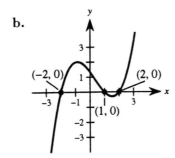

c.

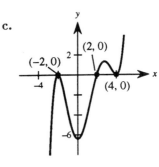

8. Use a computer/calculator to graph $x^2 + y^2 - 4x = 0$ and the given equation in the same viewing rectangle. Use the zoom feature to approximate the coordinates of any points of intersection. (Round your results to three decimal places.)

a. $x + y - 4 = 0$

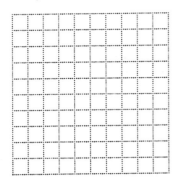

b. $x - \sqrt{3}y + 2 = 0$

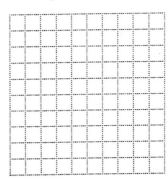

c. $2x - 3y + 5 = 0$

d. $y = 2 - (x - 2)^2$

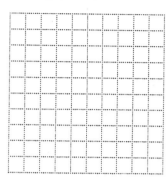

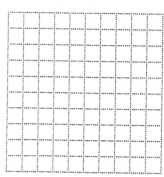

9. The data from a study measuring the relationship between the wattage x of a standard incandescent lamp and the time rate of flow of luminous energy y (in lumens) is given in the table. (*Source:* Standard Handbook for Mechanical Engineers) Three mathematical models for analyzing these data are given in parts **a–c**.

Use a computer/calculator to plot the points and graph each of the following equations. From the graphs, determine which of the models **a–c** "best fits" the data.

x	25	40	60	75	100	150	200	300	500
y	266	470	840	1150	1750	2700	4000	6000	10,500

a. $y = (19.775 + 0.179x)^2$

b. $y = -119.269 + 23.601x - 52.721\sqrt{x}$

c. $y = -3650.250 + 583.115\sqrt{x}$

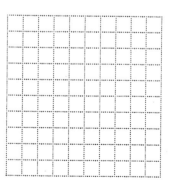

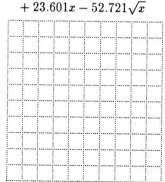

This worksheet uses 2D function grapher with zoom and solve features.

Name _____

Date _____

1. Use a computer/calculator to graph the equation $y = 5x - 3$ in the given viewing rectangle. Which viewing rectangle gives the appearance of a steeper slope? Explain why the slopes appear different.

a.

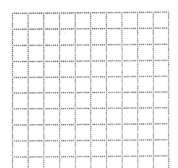

```
RANGE
Xmin=-5
Xmax=10
Xscl=1
Ymin=-10
Ymax=5
Yscl=1
```

b.

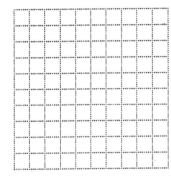

```
RANGE
Xmin=-10
Xmax=10
Xscl=2
Ymin=-100
Ymax=100
Yscl=25
```

2. The table gives the total revenues y (in millions of dollars) for H & R Block, Inc. for the years 1982 through 1992 where t is time in years with $t = 2$ corresponding to 1982. (*Source:* 1992 Annual Report for H & R Block, Inc.)

Year	1982	1983	1984	1985	1986	1987	1988	1989	1990	1991	1992
t	2	3	4	5	6	7	8	9	10	11	12
y	319	343	419	497	615	722	813	900	1053	1191	1371

a. Use a computer/calculator to plot the data and graph the linear model $y = 13.85 + 105.07t$.

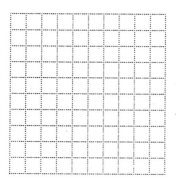

b. Interpret the y-intercept and slope of the graph within the context of the data.

c. Use the model to estimate total revenue for 1993 assuming that the model remains valid.

d. Graph the model $y = 33.85 + 105.56t$. If this were the model for the data, how would the estimate for total revenue in 1993 differ from the estimate given by the model in part **a**?

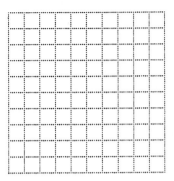

e. Graph the model $y = 13.85 + 125.07t$. If this were the model for the data, how would the estimate for total revenue in 1993 differ from the estimate given by the model in part **a**?

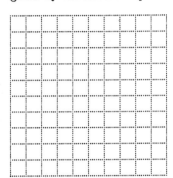

f. In the long run, does changing the y-intercept or slope have the greater effect on the model as a predictor?

3. The table gives net sales y (in millions of dollars) for Proctor & Gamble
   Company for the years 1980 through 1992 where t is time in years with
   $t = 0$ corresponding to 1980. (*Source:* 1992 Annual Report for Proctor &
   Gamble Company)

Year	1980	1981	1982	1983	1984	1985	1986
t	0	1	2	3	4	5	6
y	10,772	11,416	11,994	12,452	12,946	13,552	15,439

Year	1987	1988	1989	1990	1991	1992
t	7	8	9	10	11	12
y	17,000	19,336	21,398	24,081	27,026	29,362

   a. Plot the points and find an approximate linear model for the data.
      Graph your model.

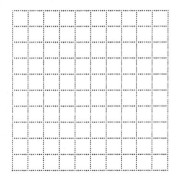

   b. Use the model to predict net sales for 1993.

The worksheet uses a 2D function grapher
with zoom and solve features.

Name _____

Date _____

In Exercises 1–10, use the function $f(x) = \dfrac{4x}{x^2+1}$ and a
computer/calculator to graph g. Determine the domain and range
of g. State whether g is odd, even, or neither.

1. $g(x) = f(x) + 2$

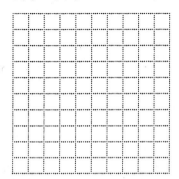

2. $g(x) = f(x+2)$

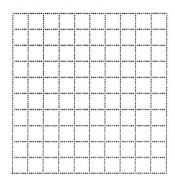

3. $g(x) = f(2x)$

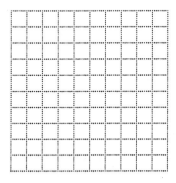

4. $g(x) = 2f(x)$

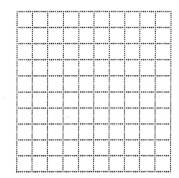

5. $g(x) = f(-x)$

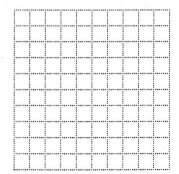

6. $g(x) = -f(x)$

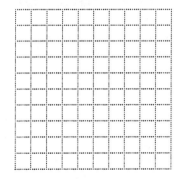

7. $g(x) = f(\sqrt{x})$

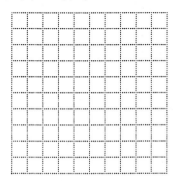

8. $g(x) = \sqrt{f(x)}$

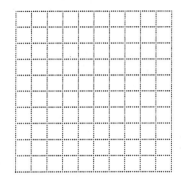

9. $g(x) = f(x^2)$

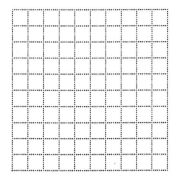

10. $g(x) = f\left(\dfrac{x-3}{2}\right)$

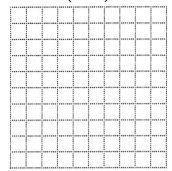

In Exercises 11–13, use the function $f(x) = -x^2 + 6x - 5$.

11. Use a computer/calculator to graph the functions f and g, where $g(x) = |f(x)|$. How do the zeros compare?

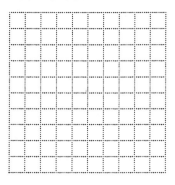

12. Use a computer/calculator to graph $g(x) = f(x - a)$ where a is a non-zero real number. How does changing the value a affect the graph? Your answer should include a statement about the relationship between the sign of a and the graph.

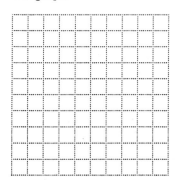

13. Use a computer/calculator to graph $g(x) = af(x)$ where a is a non-zero number. How does changing the value a affect the graph? Your answer should include a statement about the relationship between the sign of a and the graph.

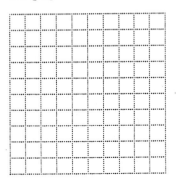

14. Use a computer/calculator to graph each function.

a. $g(x) = \begin{cases} x + 2, & -2 \le x \le -1 \\ 1 - \sqrt{1 - x^2}, & -1 < x < 1 \\ -x + 2, & 1 \le x \le 2 \end{cases}$

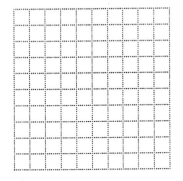

b. $f(x) = \begin{cases} \dfrac{2}{x^2 - 4x + 5}, & x \le 2 \\ x^3 - 6x^2 + 12x - 7, & x > 2 \end{cases}$

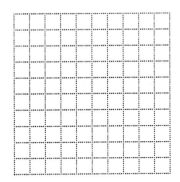

15. Consider the repeated composition of $f(x) = \sqrt{x} + k$ with itself defined by

$$f_n(x) = \underbrace{f(f(f(\cdots f(x)\cdots)))}_{n \text{ times}}.$$

Use a computer/calculator to complete the tables.

a. Let $k = \frac{1}{4}$.

n	1	2	3	4	5	6	7	8	9	10
$f_n(0)$										

b. Let $k = 9$.

n	1	2	3	4	5	6	7	8	9	10
$f_n(0)$										

c. Describe the results obtained in parts **a** and **b**.

This worksheet uses a 2D function grapher with zoom and solve features.

Name _____

Date _____

1. Use a computer/calculator to graph simultaneously the left and right sides of the equation. What can you conclude?

a. $\cos x = \sin\left(x + \dfrac{\pi}{2}\right)$

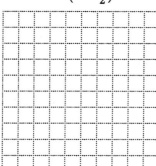

b. $\cos 2x = \cos^2 x - \sin^2 x$

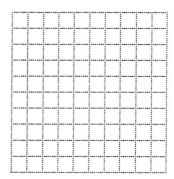

2. Use a computer/calculator to graph $f(x) = \sin x$ and $g(x) = \sqrt{1 - \cos^2 x}$. Over which intervals do the functions coincide?

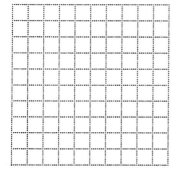

3. Use the zoom feature of a computer/calculator to approximate the zeros of the function in the interval $[0, 6]$. (Round your results to three decimal places.)

a. $f(x) = \dfrac{x}{2}(\cos \pi x - \sin \pi x)$

b. $g(x) = \dfrac{3}{4}x - \cos \pi x + \sin \dfrac{\pi x}{2}$

4. If there is a least positive number p for which $f(t + p) = f(t)$ for all t [or $f(t)$ and $f(t + p)$ are both undefined], then f is said to be periodic with period p. Consider the function

$$f(t) = \sin \dfrac{2\pi t}{3} - 2 \cos \dfrac{3\pi t}{4}$$

which models wave motion subject to amplitude modulation. Use a computer/calculator to graph $y = f(t)$ and $y = f(t + p)$ for various values of p. Find the period of the function by determining the smallest positive value of p for which the graphs coincide.

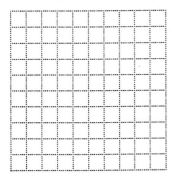

5. On average, the total number of heating degree days (base 65°), y, by month, t, for Erie, Pennsylvania is given in the table (*Source:* National Oceanic and Atmospheric Administration)

Month	Jan	Feb	Mar	Apr	May	Jun	Jul	Aug	Sep	Oct	Nov	Dec
t	1	2	3	4	5	6	7	8	9	10	11	12
y	1256	1120	977	603	323	80	17	28	130	420	729	1085

a. Use a computer/calculator to plot the ordered pairs (t, y).

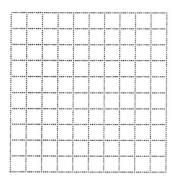

b. Fit a cosine model

$$y = a \cos(bt - c) + d$$

to the data. Start by determining the period of the function. Then try different estimates for a, c, and d and graph each trial model until you find one that is relatively accurate.

This worksheet uses a 2D function grapher with zoom and solve featuers.

Name _____

Date _____

In Exercises 1–6, use a computer/calculator to graph the function. Use the graph to determine whether the limit exists. If $\lim\limits_{x \to a} f(x)$ does exist, make a table using suitable values of x to the right and left of a to estimate the limit.

1. $\lim\limits_{x \to 1} \dfrac{x - 1}{x^2 - 3x + 2}$

x						
$f(x)$						

2. $\lim\limits_{x \to 4} \dfrac{\sqrt{x} - 2}{x - 4}$

x						
$f(x)$						

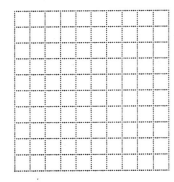

3. $\displaystyle\lim_{x \to 0} \sin \frac{1}{x}$

x						
$f(x)$						

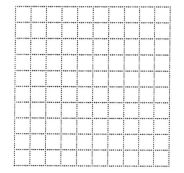

4. $\displaystyle\lim_{x \to 0} \frac{\tan x}{x}$

x						
$f(x)$						

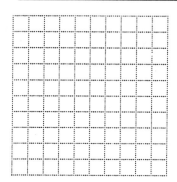

5. $\displaystyle\lim_{x \to 0} f(x)$ where

$$f(x) = \begin{cases} x + 1, & x < 0 \\ \cos x, & x \geq 0 \end{cases}$$

x						
$f(x)$						

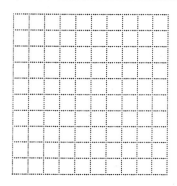

6. $\displaystyle\lim_{x \to 2} f(x)$ where

$$f(x) = \begin{cases} \dfrac{3}{x}, & 0 < x < 2 \\ -\dfrac{1}{2}x + 2, & x \geq 2 \end{cases}$$

x						
$f(x)$						

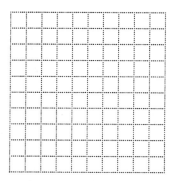

7. The statement $\lim\limits_{x \to 0} \sqrt{x+1} = 1$ means that for each $\epsilon > 0$ there exists a $\delta > 0$ such that if

$$0 < |x - 0| < \delta, \quad \text{then } |\sqrt{x+1} - 1| < \epsilon.$$

By letting $\epsilon = 0.0001$ it follows that

$$|\sqrt{x+1} - 1| < 0.0001.$$

Use a computer/calculator to graph each side of this inequality. Use the zoom feature to find an interval $(-\delta, \delta)$ in which the graph of the left side is below the graph of the right side.

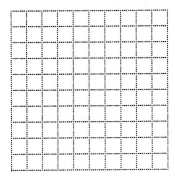

In Exercises 8–11, find the limit. Use the procedure from Exercise 7 and the definition of the limit to find the δ-interval for $\epsilon = 0.001$.

8. $\displaystyle\lim_{x \to -1} (1 - 2x)$

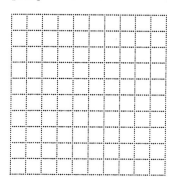

9. $\displaystyle\lim_{x \to 2} \frac{4}{x}$

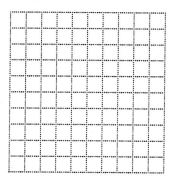

10. $\displaystyle\lim_{x \to 8} \sqrt[3]{x}$

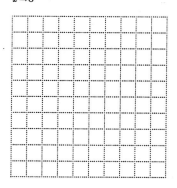

11. $\displaystyle\lim_{x \to 0} \frac{\sin x}{x}$

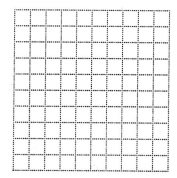

This worksheet uses a 2D function grapher with zoom and solve features.

Name _____

Date _____

In Exercises 1–6, use a computer/calculator to graph the function. Use the graph to determine whether the limit exists. If $\lim\limits_{x \to a} f(x)$ does exist, make a table using suitable values of x to the right and left of a to estimate the limit.

1. $\lim\limits_{x \to 2} \dfrac{x^2 - x - 2}{x - 3}$

x						
$f(x)$						

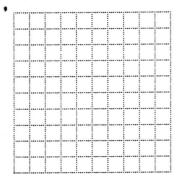

2. $\lim\limits_{x \to 3} \dfrac{9 - x^2}{1 - \sqrt{x/3}}$

x						
$f(x)$						

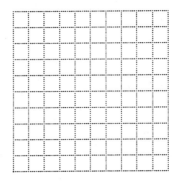

3. $\lim\limits_{x \to 3} \dfrac{x^2 - 9}{|x - 3|}$

x							
$f(x)$							

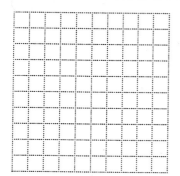

4. $\lim\limits_{x \to -2} \dfrac{x|x + 2|}{x + 2}$

x							
$f(x)$							

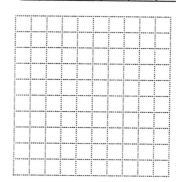

5. $\lim\limits_{x \to 0} \dfrac{[(x + 2)/(x + 3)] - 2/3}{x}$

x							
$f(x)$							

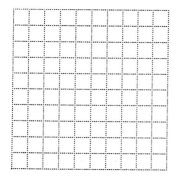

6. $\lim\limits_{x \to 0} \dfrac{\sqrt{x + 4} - 2}{x}$

x							
$f(x)$							

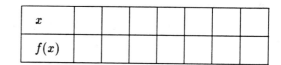
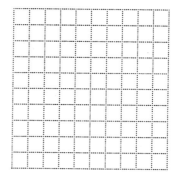

7. Explain why the following statement is true.

$$\lim_{x \to 3} \frac{x^2 - 9}{x^7 - 3x^6 + 6x^5 - 18x^4 + 12x^3 - 36x^2 + 8x - 24} = \lim_{x \to 3} \frac{x + 3}{x^6 + 6x^4 + 12x^2 + 8}$$

8. Use a computer/calculator to graph $f(x) = |x - \pi| \cos x$, $g(x) = x - \pi$, and $h(x) = \pi - x$ on the same viewing rectangle. Determine

$$\lim_{x \to \pi} |x - \pi| \cos x.$$

What theorem does this demonstrate?

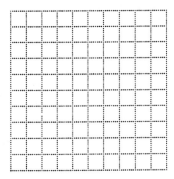

9. Use a computer/calculator to graph the function $f(x) = (\sin kx)/x$ for $k = 1$, 5, and 5/2. Use the results to make a conjecture about

$$\lim_{x \to 0} \frac{\sin kx}{x}$$

where k is a positive integer.

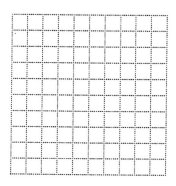

10. Determine the positive integer values of k for which the limit exists:

$$\lim_{x \to 0} \frac{1 - \cos x}{x^k}.$$

This worksheet uses a 2D function grapher with zoom and solve features.

Name _____

Date _____

In Exercises 1–6, use a computer/calculator to graph the function. From the graph, estimate $\lim\limits_{x \to c^-} f(x)$ and $\lim\limits_{x \to c^+} f(x)$. Does the function appear continuous? Is it continuous?

1. $f(x) = \dfrac{3x}{\sqrt{x^2 + 5}}$, $c = 2$

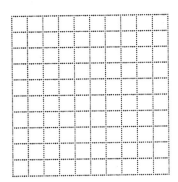

2. $f(x) = \dfrac{x - 1}{x^2 + \sqrt{x} - 2}$, $c = 1$

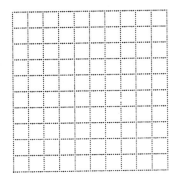

3. $f(x) = \dfrac{(x^2 - 1)|x|}{x}$, $c = 0$

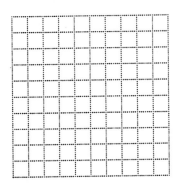

4. $f(x) = \dfrac{|x^2 - 1|x}{x - 1}$, $c = 1$

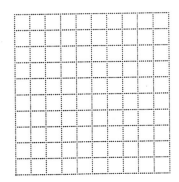

5. $f(x) = \begin{cases} x^3 + 1, & x < 1 \\ 2 - \frac{1}{3}(x-1)^3, & x \geq 1, \end{cases}$ $c = 1$

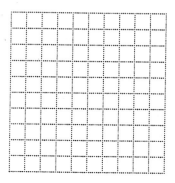

6. $f(x) = \begin{cases} -x\sqrt{x+4}, & x < 0 \\ 3x^{2/3} - 2x + 1, & x \geq 0, \end{cases}$ $c = 0$

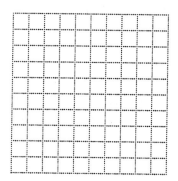

7. Find values of $a, b, c,$ and d so that f is continuous. Use a computer/calculator to graph the result.

$$f(x) = \begin{cases} \sqrt{ax + b}, & x < -4 \\ \sqrt{16 - x^2}, & -4 \leq x \leq 4 \\ \sqrt{cx + d}, & x > 4 \end{cases}$$

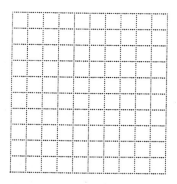

8. Find values of $a, b, c,$ and d so that f is continuous. Use a computer/calculator to graph the result.

$$f(x) = \begin{cases} ax + b, & x < -\frac{\pi}{4} \\ \tan x, & -\frac{\pi}{4} \leq x \leq \frac{\pi}{4} \\ cx + d, & x > \frac{\pi}{4} \end{cases}$$

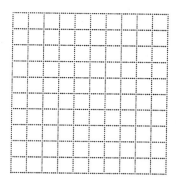

This worksheet uses a 2D function grapher with zoom and solve features.

Name _____

Date _____

In Exercises 1–4, (a) use a computer/calculator to graph the function. (b) Identify any vertical asymptotes of the function. (c) Determine whether $f(x)$ approaches ∞ or $-\infty$ as x approaches each asymptote from the left and from the right.

1. $f(x) = \left(\dfrac{x}{x-3} \right)^2$

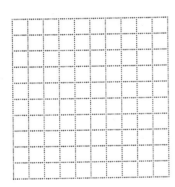

2. $f(x) = -\left(\dfrac{x-1}{x+2} \right)^2$

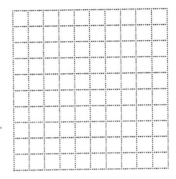

3. $f(x) = \sec \dfrac{\pi x}{4} + \csc \dfrac{\pi x}{4}, \quad -3 \le x \le 3$

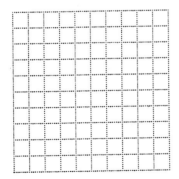

4. $f(x) = \sec \dfrac{\pi x}{2} \left(\tan \dfrac{\pi x}{2} - 1 \right), \quad -2 \le x \le 2$

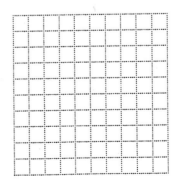

5. The statement

$$\lim_{x \to 0} \left(\frac{x}{2} + \frac{2}{x^2} \right) = \infty$$

means that for each $M > 0$ there exists a $\delta > 0$ such that $\dfrac{x}{2} + \dfrac{2}{x^2} > M$ whenever $0 < |x - 0| < \delta$.

a. Select an appropriate viewing rectangle for $M = 100$. Use the graph of the function to estimate δ.

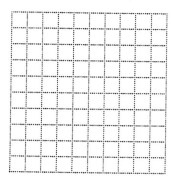

b. Select an appropriate viewing rectangle for $M = 1000$. Use the graph of the function to estimate δ.

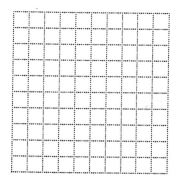

c. Write a short paragraph describing the change in δ for increasing M.

6. The statement

$$\lim_{x \to 2} \frac{x-4}{(x-2)^2} = -\infty$$

means that for each $N < 0$ there exists a $\delta > 0$ such that $\frac{x-4}{(x-2)^2} < N$ whenever $0 < |x - 2| < \delta$.

a. Select an appropriate viewing rectangle for $N = -100$. Use the graph of the function to estimate δ.

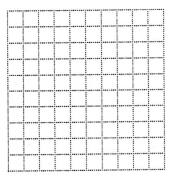

b. Select an appropriate viewing rectangle for $N = -1000$. Use the graph of the function to estimate δ.

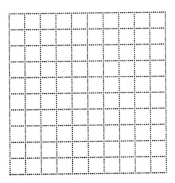

c. Write a short paragraph describing the change in δ for decreasing N.

7. On a 120-mile trip, the average speed of a truck was x mi/hr. On the return trip the average speed was y mi/hr. The average speed for the round trip was 40 mi/hr.

a. Write an equation that expresses y as a function of x.

b. Graph of the function in part a. In the context of this problem, what is the domain of the function? Identify the vertical asymptote of the function.

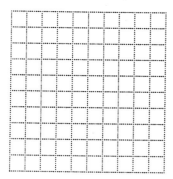

c. Given that the round trip average speed was 40 mi/hr, is it possible that the truck averaged only 20 mi/hr on the first half of the trip? Explain your answer.

This worksheet uses a 2D function grapher with zoom and solve features.

Name _____

Date _____

1. Consider the function $f(x) = \dfrac{6x}{\sqrt{x^2 + 12}}$.

    a. Use a computer/calculator to graph the function using the given viewing rectangles.

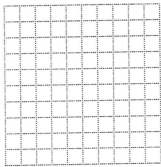

```
RANGE
Xmin=-5
Xmax=10
Xscl=1
Ymin=-10
Ymax=10
Yscl=1
```

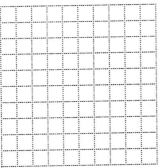

```
RANGE
Xmin=0
Xmax=6
Xscl=1
Ymin=0
Ymax=4
Yscl=1
```

    b. Estimate the slope of the tangent line to the curve at the point $(2, 3)$ for each of the graphs of part **a.** Are your estimates different and, if so, why? What can you conclude about estimating the slope of the tangent line to a graph of a function solely from a graph?

c. Use the derivative of f,

$$f'(x) = \frac{72}{(x^2 + 12)^{3/2}},$$

to find the exact slope of the tangent line to the curve at the point $(2, 3)$. Write an equation of the tangent line to the graph of f at the point $(2, 3)$. Graph the tangent line on the same viewing rectangle as the graph.

```
RANGE
Xmin=0
Xmax=6
Xscl=1
Ymin=0
Ymax=4
Yscl=1
```

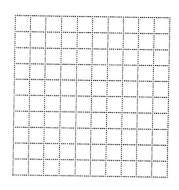

2. Consider the functions $f(x) = x(4 - x)$ and $S(x, a, \Delta x)$ where

$$S(x, a, \Delta x) = \frac{f(a + \Delta x) - f(a)}{\Delta x}(x - a) + f(a).$$

a. Graph f, $S(x, 1, 2)$, $S(x, 1, 1)$, and $S(x, 1, 0.1)$ on the same viewing rectangle.

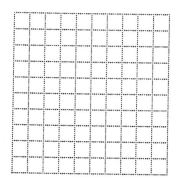

b. Graph f, $S(x, 1, -2)$, $S(x, 1, -1)$, and $S(x, 1, -0.1)$ on the same viewing rectangle.

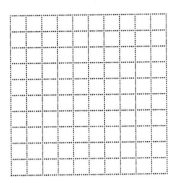

c. What are the lines of parts **a** and **b** called? List their slopes in the table.

Δx	-2	-1	-0.1	0.1	1	2
$\dfrac{f(1 + \Delta x) - f(1)}{\Delta x}$						

d. Given that $f'(x) = 4 - 2x$, determine the slope of the tangent line to the curve when $x = 1$. Describe the relationship between the slopes given in the table of part **d** and the slope of the tangent line.

3. Use a computer/calculator to graph $f(x) = |x + 1| - \frac{1}{2}|x - 2|$ and determine any points at which the function is *not* differentiable.

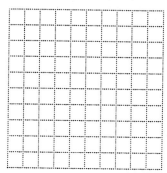

This worksheet uses a 2D function grapher and a symbolic differentiation utility.

Name _____

Date _____

In Exercises 1–6, use a computer/calculator to find the first derivative of the function. Then graph the function and its derivative on the same viewing rectangle. Describe the graph of the function at x-values that are zeros of the derivative.

1. $y = (x^2 + 3x - 2)(x^3 - 4)$

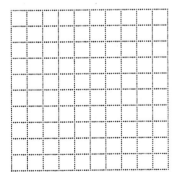

2. $y = \sqrt{x}\tan x$

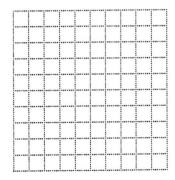

3. $f(x) = \dfrac{6x}{x^2 + 1}$

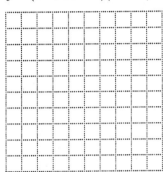

4. $g(x) = \dfrac{2x}{\sin x + \cos x}$

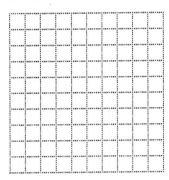

5. $f(x) = \left(\dfrac{x^2 + 5x - 2}{x^3 - 1} \right)(5x + 3)$

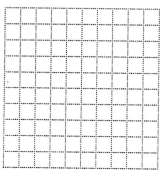

6. $h(x) = \dfrac{\sqrt{x}\,\sin x}{2x - 5}$

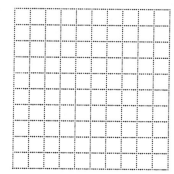

7. a. Use a computer/calculator to find the first derivative of

$$f(x) = (x^3 - 3x + 4)(x^4 + 3x^2 - 2).$$

b. Use a computer/calculator to multiply the factors of $f(x)$ in part **a.** Then find the derivative of the product. Verify that the result is equivalent to the derivative in part **a.**

8. Use a computer/calculator to determine the derivative of the function for at least the first three positive integer values of n. Use the results to write a general differentiation rule for the function.

a. $f(x) = x^n \cos x$

b. $f(x) = \dfrac{\sin x}{x^n}$

9. The table gives the air temperature, T (in degrees Fahrenheit), at various altitudes, h (in thousands of feet).

h	0	10	20	30	50	70	100
T	59.00	23.34	−24.62	−47.99	−69.70	−67.30	−50.84

a. Find the average rate of change in temperature when h increases from 0 to 10 and when h increases from 70 to 100.

b. A model for this data is

$$T = \frac{569{,}250 - 36{,}466h}{10{,}000 - 203h + 7h^2} \quad 0 \le h \le 100.$$

Graph this model and its derivative on the same viewing rectangle. Use the graph of dT/dh to estimate the altitude at which the temperature is *decreasing* at the greatest rate.

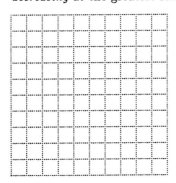

c. Use the model to estimate the instantaneous rate of change of temperature when $h = 10$.

This worksheet uses a 2D function grapher and a symbolic differentiation utility.

Name _____

Date _____

In Exercises 1–6, use a computer/calculator to find the derivative of the function. Then graph the function and its derivative on the same viewing rectangle. Describe the graph of the function at x-values that are zeros of the derivative.

1. $y = 3x\sqrt[3]{x^2 - 1}$

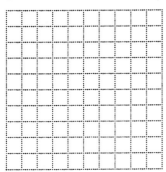

2. $y = \frac{1}{4}(x - 2)^2(x + 1)^3$

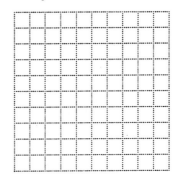

3. $f(x) = \cos(\sin x)$

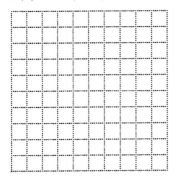

4. $f(x) = \cos\sqrt{x} - \sqrt{\cos x}, \ 0 \le x \le \frac{\pi}{2}$

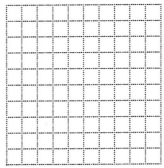

5. $g(x) = \dfrac{4}{\pi}\left(\sin\dfrac{\pi x}{2} + 13\sin\dfrac{3\pi x}{2}\right)$, $0 \le x \le 4$

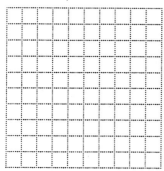

6. $h(x) = \csc\dfrac{\pi x}{4} - \sec\dfrac{\pi x}{4}$, $-2 \le x \le 2$

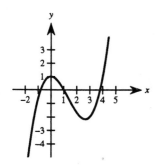

7. Use the graph of f to sketch a graph that approximates the first derivative of f.

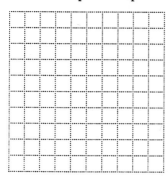

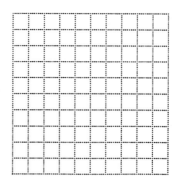

8. The normal, daily-minimum temperature, T (in degrees Fahrenheit), for Cincinnati, Ohio is given in the table. (*Source:* National Oceanographic and Atmospheric Administration)

Month	Jan	Feb	Mar	Apr	May	Jun	Jul	Aug	Sep	Oct	Nov	Dec
t	1	2	3	4	5	6	7	8	9	10	11	12
T	19.5	22.7	33.1	42.2	51.8	60.0	64.8	62.9	56.6	44.2	35.3	25.3

a. A model for this data is

$$T(t) = 43.2 - 17.89 \cos \frac{\pi t}{6} - 12.41 \sin \frac{\pi t}{6}$$

where t is time in months with $t = 1$ corresponding to January. Plot the points and graph the model on the same viewing rectangle.

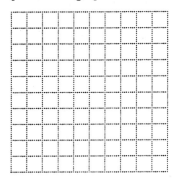

b. Find $T'(t)$ and sketch its graph. Use the derivative to complete the table.

Month	Jan	Feb	Mar	Apr	May	Jun	Jul	Aug	Sep	Oct	Nov	Dec
t	1	2	3	4	5	6	7	8	9	10	11	12
T'												

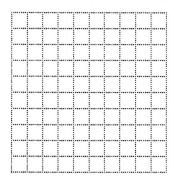

c. During what times of the year does the temperature change most rapidly? During what times does it change most slowly? Do your answers agree with your observations of temperature changes? Explain.

This worksheet uses an implicit function grapher and an implicit differentiation utility.

Name _____

Date _____

In Exercises 1–6, use implicit differentiation to write the equation of the tangent line to the graph at the specified point. Then use a computer/calculator to graph the equation and tangent line on the same viewing rectangle.

1. $x^2 + xy + y^2 - 2x = 0$

Point: $\left(1, \dfrac{-1+\sqrt{5}}{2}\right)$

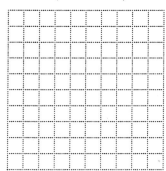

2. $x^2 - 2xy + y^2 - 2x - 2y + 1 = 0$

Point: $(2, 3 + 2\sqrt{2})$

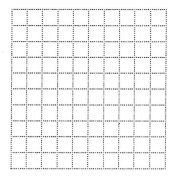

3. $\dfrac{2}{x} - \dfrac{3}{y} + x + y = 0$

Point: $(\sqrt{2}, \sqrt{5} - \sqrt{2})$

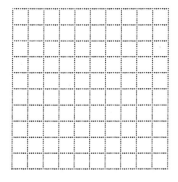

4. $y^2 = \dfrac{x^2(2-x)}{2+x}$

Point: $\left(1, \dfrac{\sqrt{3}}{3}\right)$

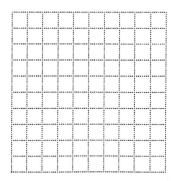

5. $y(y - \tan x) = 4$

    Point: $(0, 2)$

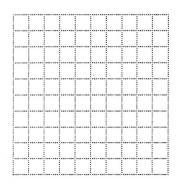

6. $y^2 = (y + 4)\sin x$

    Point: $\left(\dfrac{\pi}{2}, \dfrac{1 + \sqrt{17}}{2}\right)$

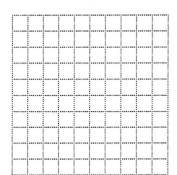

In Exercises 7 and 8, use a computer/calculator to graph the first equation for two values of C. Then graph the second equation for two values of K. Find the points of intersection of the graphs. Verify that the tangent lines to the graphs are perpendicular at these points.

7. $y = Cx^2$

    $\dfrac{x^2}{2} + y^2 = K$

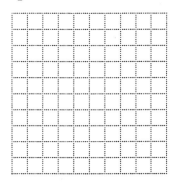

8. $x^2 + (y - C)^2 = C^2$

    $(x - K)^2 + y^2 = K^2$

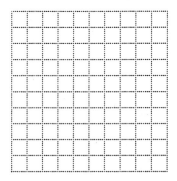

9. Consider the equation $(1 - k^2)x^2 + y^2 = 9$, where k is a real number in the interval $[0, 1)$.

a. Verify that $(3, 3k)$ is a point on the graph.

b. Graph the equation when $k = 0$, $k = 0.25$, $k = 0.50$, $k = 0.75$, and $k = 0.90$. Describe the relationship between k and the shape of the graph.

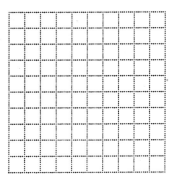

c. Find dy/dx and evaluate (if possible) the derivative at the point $(3, 3k)$ for the values of k given in the table.

k	0	0.25	0.50	0.75	0.90
$\dfrac{dy}{dx}$					

d. Determine whether the following limit exists.

$$\lim_{k \to 1} \frac{dy}{dx}$$

If it does exist, what is the limit? [In the limit, dy/dx refers to the *value* of dy/dx at the point $(3, 3k)$.]

2.6 Related Rates

Name _____

Date _____

1. An airplane flying 200 miles per hour passes directly over a radar antenna at an altitude of 1.5 miles.

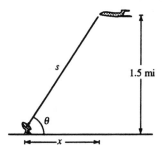

a. Use the fact that $dx/dt = -200$ to write an expression for ds/dt in terms of x.

b. Graph ds/dt as a function of x. Interpret the information that can be obtained from the graph in the context of the problem.

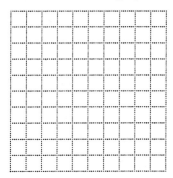

c. Use the fact that $dx/dt = -200$ to write an expression for $d\theta/dt$ in terms of x.

d. Graph $d\theta/dt$ as a function of x. Interpret the information that can be obtained from the graph in the context of the problem.

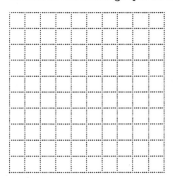

2. A spherical balloon of radius r is inflated with gas at the rate of dV/dt cubic centimeters per second.

a. Write an expression for dr/dt in terms of r and dV/dt.

b. Graph dr/dt for $r > 0$ when $dV/dt = 5$ cm^3/sec, $dV/dt = 10$ cm^3/sec, and $dV/dt = 20$ cm^3/sec on the same viewing rectangle.

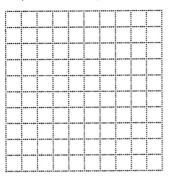

c. Write a short paragraph interpreting the result of the graphs in part **b.**

3. Describe a real-life situation in which the concept of related rates can be applied. Identify the problem you are analyzing. Use calculus to determine the related rate, and write a paragraph describing the results.

This worksheet uses a function grapher and a symbolic differentiation utility.

Name _____

Date _____

In Exercises 1–6, a. use a computer/calculator to graph the function and its derivative. b. Then, locate the absolute extrema of the function on the closed interval.

1. $f(x) = \dfrac{6x}{x^2 + 1}$

Interval: $[0, 4]$

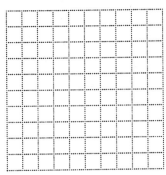

2. $g(x) = \dfrac{6x}{\sqrt{x^2 + 5}}$

Interval: $[0, 2]$

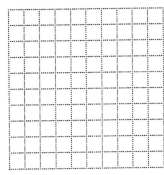

3. $g(x) = x^3 - 12x$

Interval: $[-3, 3]$

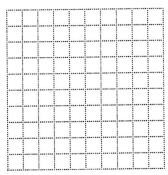

4. $g(x) = \sqrt{x^2 + 1} - x$

Interval: $[1, 3]$

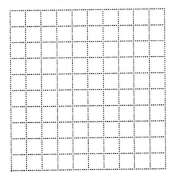

5. $f(x) = \dfrac{x}{2} + \cos x^2$

Interval: $[-1, 2]$

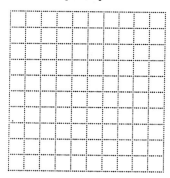

6. $f(x) = \sin\left(\dfrac{\pi x}{x^2 + 1}\right)$

Interval: $[-1, 2]$

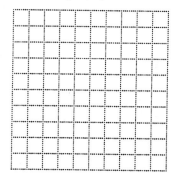

7. Consider the function $f(x) = \sin x^2$. Use a computer/calculator to graph the function $|f''(x)|$ and find its maximum on the interval $[0, 1]$. (This value is used in the error estimate for the Trapezoidal Rule.)

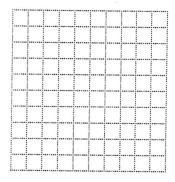

8. Consider the function $f(x) = 1/(x^4 + 1)$. Use a computer/calculator to graph the function $|f^{(4)}(x)|$ and find its maximum on the interval $[-1, 1]$. (This value is used in the error estimate for Simpson's Rule.)

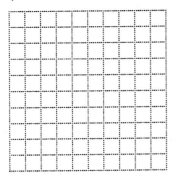

9. A weather balloon transmits the following data on the temperature, T (in degrees Fahrenheit), at altitude a (in thousands of feet).

a	20	40	60	80	100	120	160	200	240
$T(a)$	0	−65	−64	−60	−40	−30	12	−15	−100

A model for this data is

$$T(a) = 543.464 + 15.544a - 0.025a^2 - 188.266\sqrt{a}.$$

If experimental aircraft are flying in the upper atmosphere at altitudes between 100,000 and 200,000 feet, what range of temperatures will the aircraft encounter according to this model?

This worksheet uses a function grapher and a symbolic differentiation utility.

Name _____

Date _____

1. a. Use a computer/calculator to graph the function

$$f(x) = \sqrt{1 - \sin \frac{\pi x}{2}} \ .$$

What is the domain and range of f ?

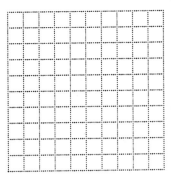

b. Use the fact that $f(0) = f(2n) = 1$ for any integer n, to determine intervals in which Rolle's Theorem applies. Use a symbolic differentiation utility to find $f'(x)$ and determine the values of c for which $f'(c) = 0$.

c. Identify intervals of the form $[2n, 2n + 2]$ on which Rolle's Theorem does not apply and explain why.

d. Use a computer/calculator to graph f'. How does the graph relate to your answer in part **c**?

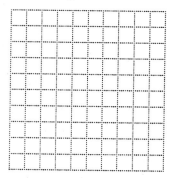

e. Evaluate, if possible, $\lim\limits_{x \to 1^-} f'(x)$ and $\lim\limits_{x \to 1^+} f'(x)$.

2. a. Use a computer/calculator to graph the function

$$f(x) = \frac{10}{x^2 + 4}$$

and find its average rate of change on the interval $[1, 4]$.

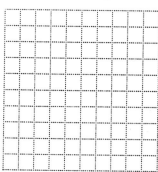

b. Find c in the interval $[1, 4]$ such that $f'(c)$ is equal to the average rate of change found in part **a**. What theorem guarantees the existence of c?

c. Sketch the secant line to the graph of f between the points $(1, f(1))$ and $(4, f(4))$. Then graph the tangent line to the curve at the point $(c, f(c))$ using the value of c found in part **b.** What is the relationship between the graph of the secant line and the graph of the tangent line?

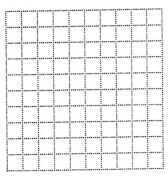

3. a. Use a computer/calculator to graph the function

$$f(x) = x^2 \sin x$$

and find its average rate of change on the interval $[-1, 1]$. Graph the secant line through the points $(-1, f(-1))$ and $(1, f(1))$.

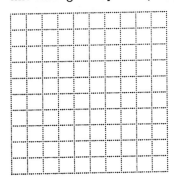

b. Find two values of c in the interval $[-1, 1]$ such that $f'(c)$ is equal to the average rate of change found in part **a.** At each value of c, graph the tangent line to the curve.

4. The bar graph gives the common stock earnings per share of Automatic Data Processing, Inc. for the years 1983 through 1992. (*Source:* ADP 1992 Annual Report)

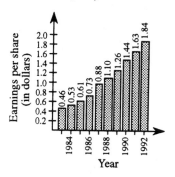

a. Find the average rate of change of the earnings per share from 1983 to 1992.

b. A mathematical model for the earnings per share is

$$E = \frac{1734 + 690t}{10,000 - 389t}, \quad 3 \leq t \leq 12$$

where t is the year with $t = 0$ corresponding to 1980. Use a computer/calculator to graph this model. Find the average rate of change of E on the interval $[3, 12]$. At which point in the interval is the instantaneous rate of change equal to the average rate of change? Compare this result to the bar graph.

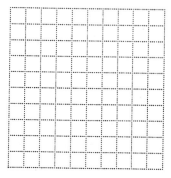

This worksheet uses a function grapher, a symbolic differentiation utility, and matrix operations.

Name _____

Date _____

In Exercises 1–6, work in small groups. One person will use a computer/calculator to graph the function and show it to the others in the group. From this graph, the members of the group will sketch an approximate graph of the derivative without finding the derivative analytically. The person with the computer/calculator will then find the derivative and sketch its graph. Within the group, compare the graph drawn by hand with the one on the utility. (Use the blank grid to sketch the graph of the derivative.)

1. $f(x) = (x-3)(x+1)$

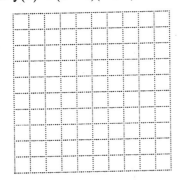

2. $f(x) = \frac{1}{3}(x+2)^2(x-2)$

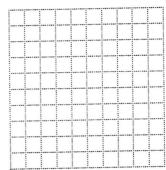

3. $g(x) = \dfrac{4x}{x^2+1}$

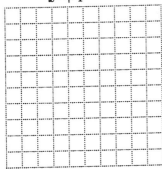

4. $g(x) = \cos \pi x$

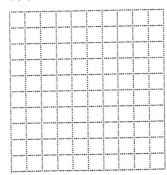

5. $h(x) = |4 - x^2|$

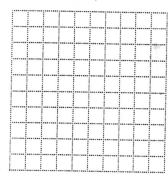

6. $h(x) = x\sqrt[3]{1 - x^2}$

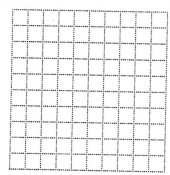

7. Write a system of equations in four unknowns to find the cubic function $f(x) = ax^3 + bx^2 + cx + d$ such that $f(1) = 7/3$, $f(3) = -3$, $f'(1) = -2$, and $f'(2) = -3$. Use a computer/calculator to solve the system for $a, b, c,$ and d. Graph the resulting cubic function.

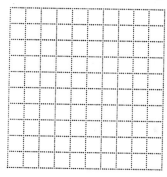

8. Public school enrollment, y (in millions), for the years 1975 to 1990 is given in the table. (*Source:* U.S. National Center for Education Statistics)

Year	1975	1976	1977	1978	1979	1980	1981	1982
y	53.7	53.0	52.4	51.3	50.7	50.3	50.0	49.3

Year	1983	1984	1985	1986	1987	1988	1989	1990
y	48.9	48.7	48.9	49.5	50.0	50.4	51.0	51.8

A mathematical model for this data is

$$y = \sqrt{6.76t^2 - 50.04t + 2501.58}$$

where t is time in years with $t = 0$ corresponding to 1980.

Use the model to estimate the year when the enrollment is minimum and compare this with the actual data.

This worksheet uses a function grapher, a symbolic differentiation utility, and solve features.

Name _____

Date _____

In Exercises 1–4, use a computer/calculator to graph the function. Then use the computer/calculator to solve the equations $f'(x) = 0$ and $f''(x) = 0$. Explain how the solutions relate to the graph of f.

1. $f(x) = \frac{1}{4}x^2(x^2 - 12)$

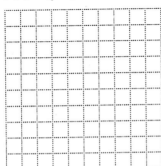

2. $f(x) = \frac{1}{2}x^2\sqrt{4 - x}$

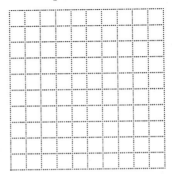

3. $f(x) = \cos(x \sin x)$, $0 \leq x \leq \pi$

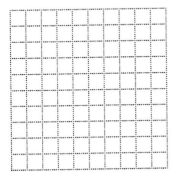

4. $f(x) = \tan\dfrac{x}{x^2 + 1}$, $0 \leq x \leq 2$

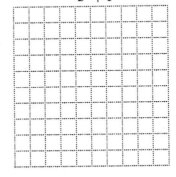

5. Consider the function $f(x) = \frac{1}{4}x^2(x^2 - 12)$.

a. Use a computer/calculator to graph f, f', and f'' on the same viewing rectangle.

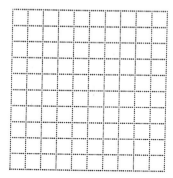

b. On which intervals is the function positive?

c. On which intervals is the function increasing?

d. On which intervals is the function concave upward?

e. The x-coordinates of the relative extrema of f' corresponds to the x-coordinates of which points on the graph of f?

6. The sales, S (in thousands of units), of a new product is modeled by

$$S = 4\left(1 + \frac{t - 4}{\sqrt{t^2 - 8t + 20}}\right)$$

where t represents time in months and $t = 0$ corresponds to the month the product is introduced. During which month do sales increase most rapidly?

7. The per capita consumption of whole milk, W (in gallons), in the United States is modeled by

$$W = (4.166 - 0.086t)^2, \ 0 \le t \le 10$$

where t is time in years and $t = 0$ corresponds to 1980. The corresponding model for consumption of lowfat milk, L (in gallons), is given by

$$L = \sqrt{81.480 + 6.921t + 0.088t^2}, \ 0 \le t \le 10.$$

a. Use a computer/calculator to graph both functions on the same viewing rectangle, and determine when the per capita consumption is the same for both products.

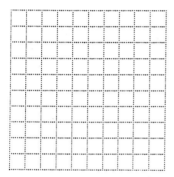

b. Compare the rates of change of the two models when $t = 10$. Use the results to estimate the change in total consumption in the nation if the population was 250 million in 1990.

This worksheet uses a function grapher.

Name _____

Date _____

In Exercises 1–4, a. use a computer/calculator to graph the function. Zoom out sufficiently far so the asymptotic behavior of the graph can be seen. b. Find any vertical or horizontal asymptotes and verify your results graphically.

1. $f(x) = \dfrac{4x^3 + 2}{2x^3 - 3x + 1}$

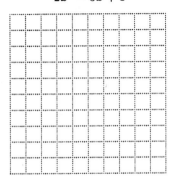

2. $f(x) = \dfrac{2 \cos x}{x^2 + 1}$

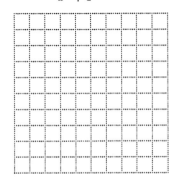

3. $g(x) = \dfrac{3x}{\sqrt{x^2 + 1}}$

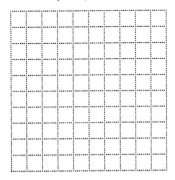

4. $h(x) = (2x + 5) - \sqrt{4x^2 + 9}$

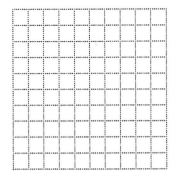

5. The tensile strength, S (in thousands of pounds per square inch), of hot-rolled nickel at selected temperatures, t (in thousands of degrees Fahrenheit), is given in the table. (*Source:* Handbook of Huntington Alloys)

t	0.07	0.60	0.80	1.00	1.20	1.50	1.80
S	73	83	76	46	34	25	8

A mathematical model for this data is given by

$$S = \frac{6918 - 3157t}{100 - 109t + 77t^2}.$$

a. Use a computer/calculator to plot the data and graph the model.

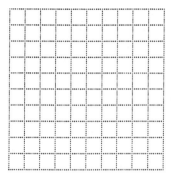

b. Describe the asymptotic behavior of this model. Is the model useful for temperatures above 2200°F? Explain.

6. The statement $\lim\limits_{x \to \infty} [(x - \cos x)/x] = 1$ means that for each $\epsilon > 0$ there exists an $M > 0$ such that

$$\left| \frac{x - \cos x}{x} - 1 \right| < \epsilon$$

whenever $x > M$.

a. Let $\epsilon = 0.01$. Use a computer/calculator to graphically approximate M. Explain the procedure you used.

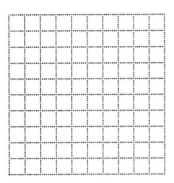

b. Repeat part **a** for $\epsilon = 0.001$.

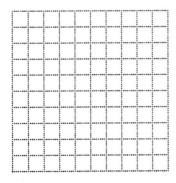

This worksheet uses a 2D function grapher and a symbolic differentiation utility.

Name _____

Date _____

In Exercises 1–6, use a computer/calculator to graph the function. Find any relative extrema, points of inflection, and asymptotes.

1. $y = (x+2)^2(x-1)^3$

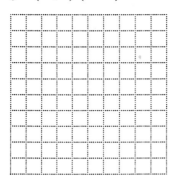

2. $y = x\sqrt[3]{1-x}$

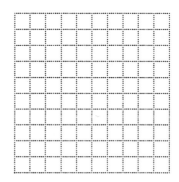

3. $f(x) = \dfrac{3(1 + \sin x)}{2 + \sin x}$

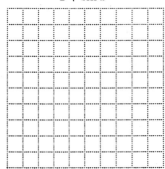

4. $f(x) = \cos^3 x^2,\ 0 \le x \le 2$

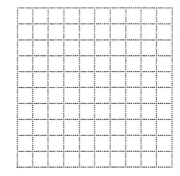

5. $g(x) = 2\left(1 - \dfrac{1}{x^2 + 1}\right)$

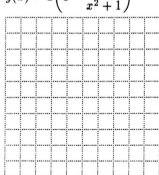

6. $g(x) = \dfrac{x^2 - 1}{x^2 + 4}$

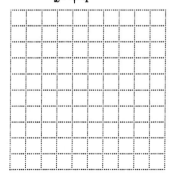

In Exercises 7 and 8, use a computer/calculator to graph the function. Zoom out sufficiently far so the graph appears to be a line. What is this line? Find its equation.

7. $g(x) = \dfrac{5 - x - x^2}{2 + x}$

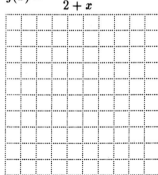

8. $g(x) = \dfrac{x^3 - 3x^2 + 4}{x^2 + 4}$

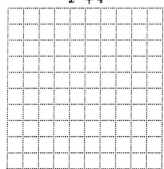

9. a. Use a computer/calculator to graph the functions

$$f(x) = x^2 + \frac{1}{x-1} \quad \text{and} \quad g(x) = x^2$$

in the viewing window $-60 \leq x \leq 60$ and $0 \leq y \leq 4000$.

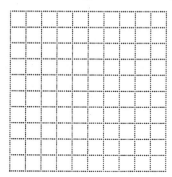

b. Find the vertical asymptote of the graph of f. Change the viewing window in part **a** so that it can be seen.

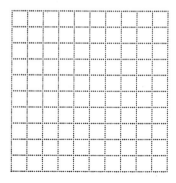

10. Consider the function $f(x) = x - \sqrt{x(ax - 1)}$.

  a. Use a computer/calculator to graph f when $a = 1$, $a = 2$, $a = 3$, $a = 1/2$, and $a = 1/4$.

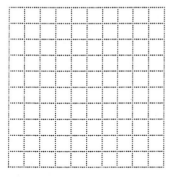

  b. Determine the value of a so that the graph of f has a horizontal asymptote.

  c. Determine the values of a so the graph of f has a slant asymptote with positive slope.

  d. Find an equation of the asymptote for each graph in part **a.**

This worksheet uses a 2D function grapher and a symbolic differentiation utility.

Name _____

Date _____

1. An open box with locking tabs is made from a 12-inch square piece of material. This is done by cutting equal squares from all corners and folding along the dashed lines shown in the figure.

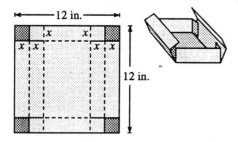

   a. Write the volume of the box as a function of x.

   b. Use a computer/calculator to graph the function of part a. Use the graph to approximate the dimensions of the box of maximum value.

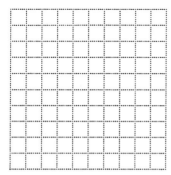

c. Find the critical number of the function of part **a** required to find the dimensions of the box of maximum volume.

2. A right circular cylinder of maximum volume is inscribed in a sphere of radius 12 meters.

   a. Use a computer/calculator to graph the equation representing the volume. Use the graph to approximate the dimensions of the cylinder of maximum volume.

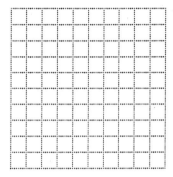

   b. Find the dimensions of the required cylinder by finding the critical number of the equation representing the volume.

3. A large room contains two speakers that are 20 feet apart and one speaker is twice as loud as the other. Assume the louder speaker is located at $(0, 0)$ and the other is located at $(20, 0)$.

    a. Find the positions that give equal amounts of sound from both speakers. (Sound at the listener's position is directly proportional to the intensity of the source and inversely proportional to the distance from the source.)

    b. If the listener is positioned on the x-axis between the speakers, find the location where the intensity of the sound is minimum.

4. A fleeing object leaves the origin and moves up the y-axis. At the same time, a pursuer leaves the point $(1, 0)$ and moves toward the fleeing object. If the pursuer's speed is twice that of the fleeing object, the equation of the path is

$$y = \tfrac{1}{3}(x^{3/2} - 3x^{1/2} + 2).$$

Use a computer/calculator to graph the path of the pursuer and find the minimum distance between the pursuer and the origin.

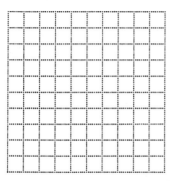

5. The location of two factories can be described as follows: the buildings are located at the points $(-7, 4)$ and $(5, 12)$ and one bank of a river is along the x-axis. To obtain cooling water, an electric generation plant is built on the riverbank. Find the point $(x, 0)$ for the position of the plant so the sum of the distances from the electric generation plant to the factories is minimum. Sketch a graph of the equation representing the sum of the distances versus the position of the generation plant.

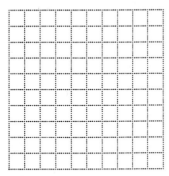

6. A hallway of width 5 feet meets a hallway of width 10 feet at right angles. It is necessary to find the length of the longest ladder that can be carried horizontally around the corner.

   a. Write the length L of the ladder as a function of θ, the angle between the ladder and the wall of the narrower hallway.

   b. Sketch a graph of the function in part **a** and use the graph to approximate the length of the longest ladder.

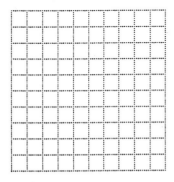

   c. Find the critical number of the function of part **a** which yields the length of the longest ladder.

7. A 1000-gallon tank is formed by adjoining two hemispheres to each end of a right circular cylinder.

    a. Write the surface area, S, of the tank as a function of the radius, r, of the cylinder.

    b. Sketch a graph of the function of part **a** and use the graph to approximate the radius of the cylinder that minimizes the surface area of the tank.

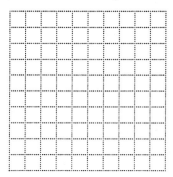

    c. Find the critical number of the function of part **a** that minimizes the surface area of the tank.

8. A person in a boat on a lake is 9 kilometers from the shore and must go to a point 12 kilometers down the shoreline in the shortest possible time (see figure). The person can walk 8 kilometers per hour and the boat can travel r kilometers per hour.

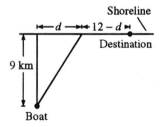

a. Assume that the person should travel by boat and by foot. Let d be the distance down the shoreline the person should strike land for the shortest total travel time. Write d as a function of r.

b. Sketch the graph of the function $d(r)$. Determine the slowest speed of the boat so the shortest possible time criteria is met by making the entire trip by water. Use this to give the domain of the function in the context of this problem.

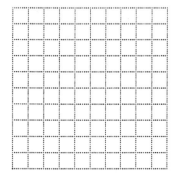

c. Determine the concavity of the graph of the function d over the domain stated in part b. What information does the concavity give about the relationship between d and r?

This worksheet uses a 2D function grapher, programming capabilities, and a symbolic differentiation utility.

Name _____

Date _____

In Exercises 1–4, use your computer/calculator and Newton's Method to approximate any real zeros of the specified function with error less than 0.0001. Graph the function to obtain the initial guess of any zeros.

1. $f(x) = 3x^3 - 5x - 3$

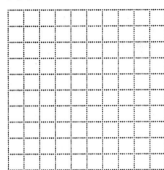

2. $g(x) = 5 - 3x^3 - x^4$

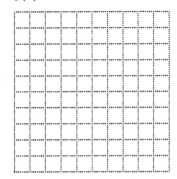

3. $g(x) = 3\sin(\pi x - 1) - \dfrac{1}{2}\cos\dfrac{\pi x}{3}$, $0 \le x \le 2$

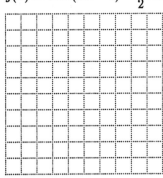

4. $h(x) = x - \tan\left(x - \dfrac{\pi}{4}\right)$, $0 \le x \le 2$

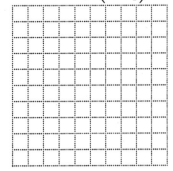

In Exercises 5 and 6, use your computer/calculator to approximate
any critical numbers of the function with error less than 0.001.

5. $h(x) = \dfrac{\sin \pi x}{x^2 + 1}$, $0 \le x \le 1$

6. $f(x) = \dfrac{1 + 2\cos x}{2 - \sin x}$, $0 \le x \le 2$

7. Consider the function $f(x) = \frac{1}{16}(x^4 - 6x^3 + 48)$.

   a. Use a computer/calculator to graph f. State the number of zeros of
      the function.

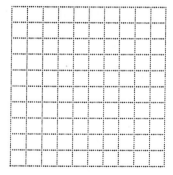

   b. Approximate a zero of the function using Newton's Method with $x_1 = 2$
      as an initial guess.

   c. Approximate a zero of the function using Newton's Method with $x_1 = 1/2$
      as an initial guess.

d. To understand why the results in parts **b** and **c** are different, sketch the tangent lines to the graph of f at the points $(2, f(2))$ and $(\frac{1}{2}, f(\frac{1}{2}))$. Find the x-intercept of each tangent line and compare the intercepts with the results of the first iteration of Newton's Method parts **b** and **c**.

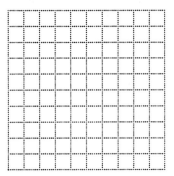

e. Write a short paragraph summarizing how Newton's Method works. Use the results of this exercise to describe why it is important to select the initial guess carefully.

8. A deposit of P dollars is made at the beginning of each month into an account at an annual interest rate r, compounded monthly. The balance A after t years is

$$A = P\left[\left(1 + \frac{r}{12}\right)^{12t} - 1\right]\left(1 + \frac{12}{r}\right).$$

A person deposited $50 per month into a mutual fund for 40 years. At that time the account had a balance of approximately $210,000. Approximate the average annual interest rate r at which the fund appreciated over the 40 years.

This worksheet uses a 2D function grapher and a symbolic differentiation utility.

Name _____

Date _____

1. Consider the function $f(x) = x\sqrt{5-x}$.

    a. Use a computer/calculator to graph the function.

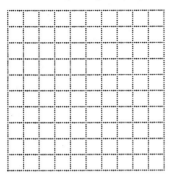

    b. Find an equation for the tangent line T to the curve at the point $(1, 2)$ and complete the following table.

x	0.5	0.9	1	1.1	1.5
$f(x)$					
$T(x)$					
$T(x) - f(x)$					

c. Find an equation for the tangent line T to the curve at the point $(4, 4)$ and complete the following table.

x	3.5	3.9	4	4.1	4.5
$f(x)$					
$T(x)$					
$T(x) - f(x)$					

d. Which tangent line is a better approximation at "small" equal distances from the point of tangency? Explain.

In Exercises 2–5, use the information to evaluate Δy and dy. Use a computer/calculator to graph the function and the tangent line to the curve at the specified value of x. Zoom in sufficiently far so you can label the distances Δy and dy.

2. $y = 2 + x - \sqrt{x^2 + 1}, x = 0, \Delta x = dx = 0.05$

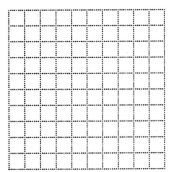

3. $y = |x^2 - 2x| - x, x = 1, \Delta x = dx = 0.1$

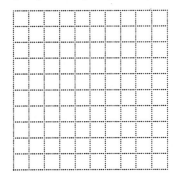

4. $y = x^2 \sin x, x = -2, \Delta x = dx = 0.5$

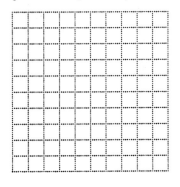

5. $y = \dfrac{x^2}{x^2 - 1}, x = 3, \Delta x = dx = 0.2$

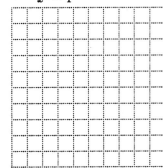

This worksheet uses a 2D function grapher and a symbolic differentiation utility.

Name _____

Date _____

1. An open box with a square base is made of a material that costs $0.75 per square foot. A double layer of the material is used in the base. The cost for sealing the four vertical edges and the four edges around the base is $0.10 per foot. The volume of the box is 5 ft^3.

   a. Write the cost of producing the box as a function of x, the length of each edge of the base.

   b. Use a computer/calculator to graph the function of part **a** and use the graph to approximate the dimensions of the box that minimizes cost.

   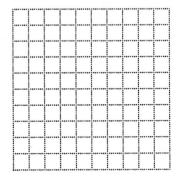

   c. Find the critical number of the function of part **a** required to find the dimensions of the box which minimizes the production cost.

2. A company uses a storage tank with a 250 gallon capacity. (1 ft^3 holds approximately 7.5 gallons.) The tank is 5 feet long and the ends are formed by rectangles with semicircles on the top and bottom (see figure). The material for fabricating the tank costs $1.20 per square foot and there is a charge of $0.90 per square foot for sealing the seams around the ends. (*Note:* The volume is length times the area of an end.)

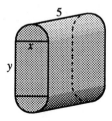

a. Write an equation for the volume in terms of x and y and solve for y.

b. Write an equation for the cost of the tank in terms of x and y. Use the result in part **a** to write the cost as a function of x.

c. Use a computer/calculator to graph the cost function and approximate the dimensions of the ends of the tank that costs the least to manufacture.

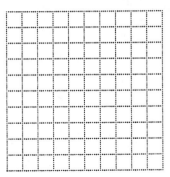

d. Use a computer/calculator to differentiate and solve for the critical number of the cost function. Use the result to determine the optimal shape of the cross-sections of the tank.

e. If the company makes a 50% markup on cost, determine the selling price of a tank.

3. The location of a fuel distribution center can be described as follows: it is located at the origin of the rectangular coordinate system (units in miles). The center supplies four factories located at $(-1, 4), (3, -1), (4, 3),$ and $(5, 2)$, respectively. A trunk line runs from the distribution center along the line $y = mx$. Feeder lines run perpendicular to the trunk line to each of the four factories (see figure).

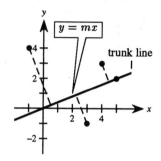

a. The distance from a point (x_1, y_1) to the line $Ax + By + C = 0$ is given by

$$\frac{|Ax_1 + By_1 + C|}{\sqrt{A^2 + B^2}}.$$

Write the sum S of the lengths of the feeder lines as a function of m.

b. Use a computer/calculator to graph the function S. Use the graph to find the value of m so S is minimized. Determine the minimal value of S.

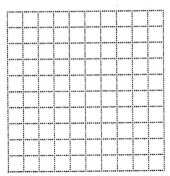

4. The demand function for a product is

$$p = \frac{1000}{x + 324}$$

where p is the selling price of the product and x is the demand. The cost function is $C = 0.42x + 15$.

a. Find the equation giving the profit P as a function of x. Use a computer/calculator to graph the function.

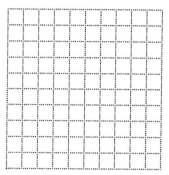

b. Use a computer/calculator to determine the price that maximizes the profit.

This worksheet uses a 2D function grapher and symbolic integration capabilities.

Name _____

Date _____

In Exercises 1–6, evaluate the indefinite integral a. without the use of a computer/calculator and b. by using a computer/calculator. If the answers differ in form, verify that they are equivalent.

1. $\displaystyle\int (x^4 - 4.6x + 10.8)\, dx$

2. $\displaystyle\int (y^2 + 2)(2y - 5)\, dy$

3. $\displaystyle\int \frac{3}{x\sqrt{x}}\, dx$

4. $\displaystyle\int \frac{6z^2 - 5\sqrt{z}}{z}\, dz$

5. $\displaystyle\int (\sqrt[3]{x} - 3\cos x)\, dx$

6. $\displaystyle\int \csc\theta(\cot\theta - \csc\theta)\, d\theta$

In Exercises 7–10, use a computer/calculator to **a.** graph the derivative, **b.** graph the antiderivative for three different values of the constant of integration, and **c.** find an equation for y that passes through the point (2, 3).

7. $\dfrac{dy}{dx} = \dfrac{x}{2} - 1$

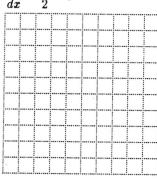

8. $\dfrac{dy}{dx} = \dfrac{1}{x^2}$

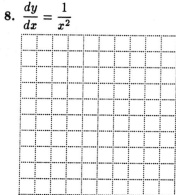

9. $\dfrac{dy}{dx} = 2 \sin x$

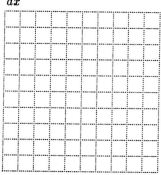

10. $\dfrac{dy}{dx} = \dfrac{1}{4} \sec^2 x$

11. Make some observations about the graphs in Exercises 7–10. **a.** For example, describe the relationship between the sign of the derivative and the behavior of the antiderivatives. **b.** What is the relationship between the tangent lines to the antiderivatives for a specific value of x?

12. A car traveling at 60 miles per hour was brought to a stop, at constant deceleration, 120 feet from where the brakes were applied. How far had the car moved when its speed was reduced to **a.** 45 miles per hour and **b.** 15 miles per hour? **c.** Draw the real number line from 0 to 120, and plot the points found in parts **a** and **b** What conclusions can you draw?

*This worksheet uses programming
capabilities.*

Name _____

Date _____

**In Exercises 1 and 2, use the summation capabilities of your
computer/calculator to evaluate the sum. Then, use the
summation formulas for sums of powers of integers to find the sum.
Verify that the two methods yield the same sum.**

1. $\displaystyle\sum_{i=1}^{25} i^2$ **2.** $\displaystyle\sum_{i=1}^{18} i^3$

3. You are required to approximate the area of the region bounded by the
graphs of $f(x) = x^{2/3} - 1$, $x = 8$, and $y = 0$.

   a. Complete and shade the rectangles representing the lower sum with $n = 7$
in the accompanying figure. Find this lower sum.

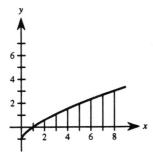

b. Complete and shade the rectangles representing the upper sum with $n = 7$ in the accompanying figure. Find this upper sum.

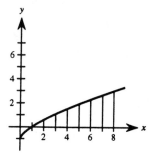

c. Complete and shade the rectangles whose heights are determined by the functional values at the midpoint of each subinterval when with $n = 7$ in the accompanying figure. Find this sum using the Midpoint Rule.

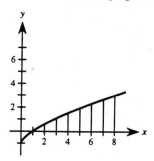

d. Use a computer/calculator and the accompanying sums to complete the following table of approximations of the area.

Lower sum: $s(n) = \sum_{i=1}^{n} f\left[1 + (i-1)\frac{7}{n}\right]\left(\frac{7}{n}\right)$

Upper sum: $S(n) = \sum_{i=1}^{n} f\left[1 + (i)\frac{7}{n}\right]\left(\frac{7}{n}\right)$

Midpoint: $M(n) = \sum_{i=1}^{n} f\left[1 + \left(i - \frac{1}{2}\right)\frac{7}{n}\right]\left(\frac{7}{n}\right)$

n	5	10	50	100	250	500
$s(n)$						
$S(n)$						
$M(n)$						

e. Explain why $s(n)$ increases and $S(n)$ decreases when n increases. Which sum yields the best approximation of the actual area, 11.6, for a given value of n? Explain your answer.

4. Use a computer/calculator to complete the following table of approximations of the area of the region bounded by the graphs of $y = 6x/(x^2 + 2), y = 0, x = 2$, and $x = 4$. When finding the formulas for the upper and lower sums, note that the function is decreasing for $2 \le x \le 4$.

n	5	10	50	100	250	500
$s(n)$						
$S(n)$						
$M(n)$						

This worksheet uses a 2D function grapher and programming capabilities.

Name _____

Date _____

In this laboratory, use a computer/calculator to approximate the definite integrals using the Riemann sum

$$\sum_{i=1}^{n} f(c_i)\Delta x_i$$

where the subintervals are of equal width. Obtain three approximations of the integral where c_i is the left-hand endpoint, midpoint, and right-hand endpoint of each subinterval. Denote these by $L(n)$, $M(n)$, and $R(n)$, respectively.

In Exercises 1–4, complete the table of approximations of the definite integral. (The value of the integral, accurate to 4 decimal places, is given.)

1. $\int_0^3 \dfrac{14x}{x^3+1}\, dx \approx 12.3044$

n	4	8	12	20	30	40
$L(n)$						
$M(n)$						
$R(n)$						

2. $\int_0^2 \sqrt{8-x^3}\, dx \approx 4.7592$

n	4	8	12	20	30	40
$L(n)$						
$M(n)$						
$R(n)$						

3. $\displaystyle\int_0^{\pi/2} x^2 \cos x\,dx \approx 0.4674$

n	4	8	12	20	30	40
$L(n)$						
$M(n)$						
$R(n)$						

4. $\displaystyle\int_0^{\pi} \frac{x}{1+\sin x}\,dx \approx 3.1416$

n	4	8	12	20	30	40
$L(n)$						
$M(n)$						
$R(n)$						

5. Determine if $L(n)$ and $R(n)$ over-estimate or under-estimate a definite integral on an interval where the integrand is a decreasing function. Give a reason for your answer. Answer the question if the integrand is an increasing function on the interval of integration.

6. Consider the integral

$$\int_{-2}^{2} \frac{5x}{x^2+1}\,dx.$$

    a. Evaluate $L(4)$, $L(10)$, and $L(40)$.

b. Graph the integrand showing the partition for $L(4)$.

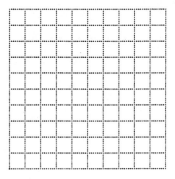

c. Use the results of parts **a.** and **b.** to determine what $L(n)$ is approaching as n increases. Give a reason for your answer.

7. Consider the integral

$$\int_0^3 (x^2 - 4x)\,dx.$$

Graph the integrand. From the graph, give the sign of the definite integral. Demonstrate your answer by obtaining the approximations $L(20)$, $M(20)$, and $R(20)$.

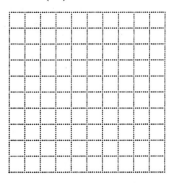

8. a. Use the symbolic summation capabilities of a computer algebra system to find expressions for $L(n)$ and $R(n)$ given the definite integral

$$\int_0^2 (x^3 + 1)\, dx.$$

b. Use the computer to find $\lim_{n \to \infty} L(n)$ and $\lim_{n \to \infty} R(n)$, the exact value of the definite integral.

This worksheet uses a 2D function grapher and a symbolic integration utility.

Name _____

Date _____

1. Consider the definite integral $\int_{1}^{3} \left(x + \dfrac{1}{x^2} \right) dx$.

    a. Graph the integrand and from the graph state whether the value of the integral is positive or negative.

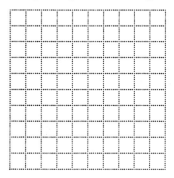

    b. Evaluate the integral without the aid of a symbolic integration utility.

    c. Use a computer/calculator with symbolic integration capabilities to evaluate the integral.

d. Let $M(n)$ represent the Riemann Sum as defined in laboratory 4.3.
Complete the following table. [The error is the magnitude of the difference
between $M(n)$ and the answers in parts b and c.]

n	2	4	10	20	50	100
$M(n)$						
Error						
% Error						

e. What factors, other than the number of partitions n, do you think may
determine the accuracy of a Riemann Sum in approximating a definite
integral?

2. a. Use a computer/calculator to graph the function

$$f(x) = 3x^{2/3}(2 - x^{1/3})$$

and find its average value over the interval [0, 8]. Graph the horizontal line
representing the average value.

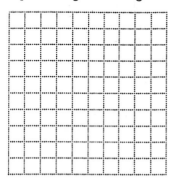

b. Find all values of x for which the function equals its average value.

3. The length of the stroke of a hydraulic press is 24 inches. The force, F (in pounds), of the press at 3 inch increments x, is given in the following table.

x	0	3	6	9	12	15	18	21	24
F	0	500	2150	8900	18,000	21,200	24,500	25,250	24,600

There is concern about the reliability of the press when the required force is great. A continuous model for the upper range of the data is given by

$$F = 335 + 5{,}540x - 99x^2 - 10{,}449\sqrt{x}, \quad 9 \le x \le 24$$

Use a computer/calculator to find the average force over the last 12 inches of the cycle of the press.

4. Consider the function given by $F(x) = \displaystyle\int_0^x \frac{t}{2}\, dt$ where $x \ge 0$.

    a. Find the function F. Since $f(t) \ge 0$ over the interval of integration $[0, x]$, $F(x)$ represents an area. Demonstrate this by comparing $F(6)$ with the area of the appropriate triangle.

b. Graph the functions $f(t) = t/2$ and $F(x)$. Discuss the rate of increase of the area under the line as x increases.

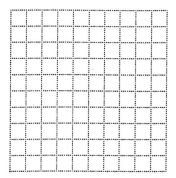

5. Consider the function given by $F(x) = \displaystyle\int_0^x \sin t \, dt$ where $0 \le x \le 2\pi$.

a. Find the function F. Graph the functions $f(t) = \sin t$ and $F(x)$.

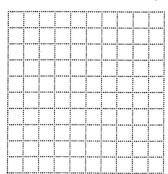

b. Identify and give a reason for the behavior of F when $f(t)$ is positive.

c. Identify and give a reason for the behavior of F when $f(t)$ is negative.

d. Identify and give a reason for the behavior of F at the zero of $f(t)$.

e. Give a geometric argument for $F(2\pi) = 0$.

This worksheet uses a 2D function grapher and a symbolic integration utility.

Name _____

Date _____

In Exercises 1 and 2, use a computer/calculator to evaluate the indefinite integral. Check the result by differentiating without the aid of a symbolic differentiation utility.

1. $\displaystyle\int x^2\sqrt{3x-2}\,dx$

2. $\displaystyle\int \left(3\sin\frac{\pi t}{6} - 2\cos\frac{\pi t}{3}\right) dt$

In Exercises 3 and 4, graph the function and find the area of the region bounded by the function and the x-axis on the specified interval.

3. $f(x) = x\sqrt{6-x},\ 0 \le x \le 6$

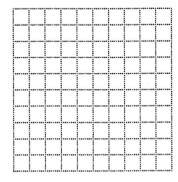

4. $h(x) = \sin\dfrac{\pi x}{2} - \dfrac{1}{3}\sin\dfrac{3\pi x}{2},\ 0 \le x \le 2$

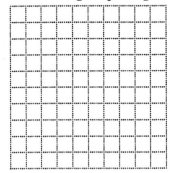

5. A farmer kept a log of his daily diesel-fuel use for 1 year. Based on this data, the consumption, C (in gallons), is modeled by

$$C = 30.3 + 21.6 \sin\left(\frac{2\pi t}{365} + 10.9\right)$$

where t is time in days with $t = 1$ corresponding to January 1.

a. Graph the function and approximate the maximum daily usage of diesel fuel.

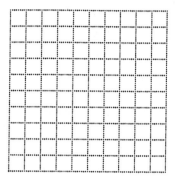

b. Approximate the average daily usage of fuel throughout 1 year.

c. The following model is programmed into the computer of the diesel fuel supplier to automatically signal delivery dates. The farmer has a 1000-gallon fuel tank and the signal for a delivery should occur when approximately 250 gallons remain. Suppose the tank was filled on day a. The next delivery should occur on day t where t is the solution to the equation

$$\int_a^t \left[30.3 + 21.6 \sin\left(\frac{2\pi x}{365} + 10.9 \right) \right] dx = 750.$$

Suppose the tank was filled on April 5 ($a = 95$). Estimate the date when the next delivery should occur.

This worksheet uses a 2D function grapher and symbolic differentiation and integration utilities.

Name _____

Date _____

In this laboratory, use a computer/calculator to approximate the definite integrals. Using the definitions of $L(n)$, $M(n)$, and $R(n)$ from lab 4.3, the Trapezoidal Rule can be written as

$$T(n) = \frac{1}{2}[L(n) + R(n)]$$

and Simpson's Rule can be written as

$$S(n) = \frac{1}{3}\left[T\left(\frac{n}{2}\right) + 2M\left(\frac{n}{2}\right)\right]$$

for even n.

In Exercises 1 and 2, complete the table of approximations of the definite integral.

1. $\displaystyle\int_0^3 \frac{x}{\sqrt{x^3+1}}\,dx$

n	$L(n)$	$M(n)$	$R(n)$	$T(n)$	$S(n)$
4					
8					
12					
16					
20					

2. $\displaystyle\int_2^6 \frac{1}{\sin(x/4) + \cos(x/4)}\, dx$

n	$L(n)$	$M(n)$	$R(n)$	$T(n)$	$S(n)$
4					
8					
12					
16					
20					

3. Consider the integral $\displaystyle\int_0^\pi \frac{2\sin x}{1 + \cos^2 x}\, dx = \pi.$

a. Use a computer/calculator and the Trapezoidal Rule to complete the following table.

n	4	10	20	50	100	125
$T(n)$						
Error						

b. Use a computer/calculator to find and graph the second derivative of the integrand. Use the graph to estimate the maximum value of $|f''(x)|$ over the interval of integration. Find n so the error in approximating the definite integral using the Trapezoidal Rule is less than 0.001. Write a short paragraph comparing the value of n and the entries in the table in part **a.**

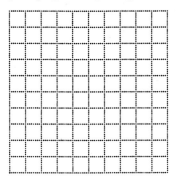

c. Use a computer/calculator and Simpson's Rule to complete the following table.

n	2	4	8	12	16	20
$S(n)$						
Error						

d. Use a computer/calculator to find and graph the fourth derivative of the integrand. Use the graph to estimate the maximum value of $|f^{(4)}(x)|$ over the interval of integration. Find n so the error in approximating the definite integral using Simpson's Rule is less than 0.001. Write a short paragraph comparing the value of n and the entries in the table in part **c.**

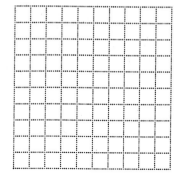

This worksheet uses a 2D function grapher and a symbolic differentiation utility.

Name _____

Date _____

1. Use a computer/calculator to complete the following table where $S(x)$ represents the approximation of the integral

$$\int_1^x \frac{1}{t}\, dt$$

by Simpson's Rule with $n = 20$ and the error is $\ln x - S(x)$.

x	0.5	1	1.5	2	2.5	3	3.5	4	4.5	5
$S(x)$										
$\ln x$										
Error										

2. Consider the functions

$$f(x) = \ln \frac{\sqrt{x^2 + 1}}{x} \quad \text{and} \quad g(x) = \frac{1}{2}\ln(x^2 + 1) - \ln x.$$

Use a computer/calculator to graph f and g. What is the relationship between the graphs, and therefore, between the functions? Give a reason for this relationship.

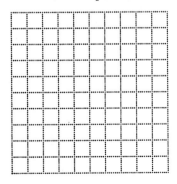

3. The table gives the percentage x of permanent antifreeze in the cooling system of an automobile and the corresponding protection to freezing y in degrees Fahrenheit. (*Source:* Standard Handbook of Mechanical Engineers)

x	20	25	33	40	50	60
y	16°	10°	0°	−12°	−34°	−62°

A model for this data is given by

$$y = -124.12 - 3.88x + 72.33 \ln x, \quad 20 \le x \le 60.$$

a. Determine the concavity of the graph of the model. Interpret your answer in the context of this exercise.

b. Can the model be used as x approaches 0? Why or why not?

4. Consider the function $f(x) = (\sin x) \ln x$, $0 < x \le 4$.

    a. Use a computer/calculator to graph the function and its derivative.

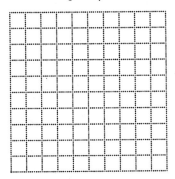

    b. Find any zeros of the function on the specified interval.

    c. Approximate any extrema of the function on the specified interval.

    d. Use the graph to determine if

$$\lim_{x \to 0^+} f(x)$$

    exists, and if it does, estimate its value.

5. Answer the following about the composition of the functions $f(x) = \sin x$ and $g(x) = \ln x$. Give reasons for your answers.

a. Determine whether $f \circ g$ or $g \circ f$ has vertical asymptotes.

b. Determine whether $f \circ g$ or $g \circ f$ is periodic.

This worksheet uses a 2D function grapher and a symbolic integration utility.

Name _____

Date _____

In Exercises 1 and 2, use a computer/calculator to evaluate the integral and graph the region whose area is given by the integral.

1. $\displaystyle\int_0^8 \frac{10x}{2x+3}\,dx$

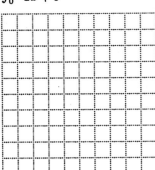

2. $\displaystyle\int_0^1 \left(\sec\frac{\pi t}{4} - \tan\frac{\pi t}{4} \right) dt$

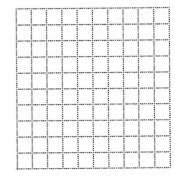

3. Consider the integral $\displaystyle\int \frac{x^n}{ax+b}\,dx$ where n is a non-negative integer and $a \neq 0$.

    a. Perform the necessary long division and evaluate the integral without the aid of a symbolic integration utility for the case when $n = 2$.

    b. Use a computer/calculator to evaluate the integral when $n = 0$, $n = 1$, $n = 3$, and $n = 4$.

c. Use the results in parts **a** and **b** to identify a pattern in the antiderivatives. Use summation notation to express the polynomial terms of the antiderivative.

d. Verify the reduction formula

$$\int \frac{x^n}{ax+b}\,dx = \frac{x^n}{na} - \frac{b}{a}\int \frac{x^{n-1}}{ax+b}\,dx.$$

4. Use a computer/calculator to graph the functions

$$f(x) = \frac{1}{x-2} \quad \text{and} \quad F(x) = \int_3^x \frac{1}{t-2}\,dt.$$

Describe and explain the relationship between the sign of $f(x)$ and the behavior of $F(x)$.

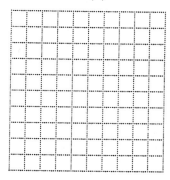

5. The continuous cash flow to meet the costs, C (in million of dollars), for producing a new product is modeled by

$$C(t) = \frac{24}{t+3} - 2, \quad 0 \le t \le 9$$

where t is time in months.

a. Approximate the total start-up cost to the corporation by evaluating the integral

$$\int_0^9 C(t)\, dt.$$

b. Management plans to borrow the money in $5 million increments. If this amount is borrowed at time a, then the approximate time t when another $5 million will be needed is the solution to the equation

$$\int_a^t \left(\frac{24}{x+3} - 2 \right) dx = 5.$$

Approximate the times when money will be borrowed if the first $5 million is borrowed at time $t = 0$.

This worksheet uses a 2D function grapher and a symbolic differentiation utility.

Name _____

Date _____

In Exercises 1 and 2, a. graph the function f and determine the largest interval $a < x < b$ containing 0 on which it has an inverse, b. find f^{-1} on the specified interval and sketch its graph, and c. graph the line $y = x$. d. What is the relationship between the graph of f over the interval found in part a. and the graph of f^{-1}?

1. $f(x) = x^2 + 2x - 2$

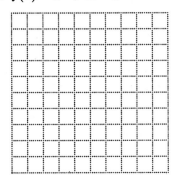

2. $f(x) = 4 - (x + 2)^{2/3}$

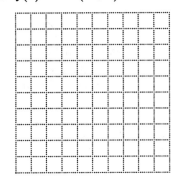

3. Consider the function $f(x) = \dfrac{x}{4}(x^4 + 3x^2 + 1)$

    a. Use calculus to verify that the function is strictly monotonic on its entire domain, and therefore, possesses an inverse.

b. For this function it is impossible to find a formula for f^{-1}. It is possible to find solution points of the inverse function. For example, since $f(1) = \frac{5}{4}$, you known that $f^{-1}(\frac{5}{4}) = 1$. To find $f^{-1}(2)$, solve the equation

$$\frac{x}{4}(x^4 + 3x^2 + 1) = 2.$$

Use this technique with a computer/calculator to complete the following table.

x	0	0.25	0.50	0.75	1.00	1.25	1.50	1.75	2.00
$f^{-1}(x)$									

c. Use a computer/calculator to graph f. Use the table from part **b** to graph f^{-1} without the aid of a graphing utility. Because of symmetry, you can graph f^{-1} for negative values of x. [With some graphing software you can graph f^{-1} without its equation. This is done by plotting $(f(x), x)$.]

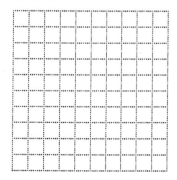

d. Find and sketch the graphs of the tangent lines to the functions f and f^{-1} at the points $(1, \frac{5}{4})$ and $(\frac{5}{4}, 1)$, respectively. Recall that

$$(f^{-1})'(x) = \frac{1}{f'(f^{-1}(x))}.$$

Add the tangent lines to the graphs in part **c**.

5.4 Exponential Functions: Differentiation and Integration

This worksheet uses a 2D function grapher, a symbolic differentiation utility and a symbolic integration utility.

Name _____

Date _____

1. A weight, hanging from a spring attached to the ceiling, is given an initial upward velocity and begins to oscillate. The displacement from its equilibrium position, y (measured in feet), is given by

$$y = 0.75e^{-0.2t}\sin(6.2t), \quad t \geq 0$$

where t is time in seconds.

a. Use a computer/calculator to graph the function. Describe the distance the weight moves with each consecutive oscillation. What is the physical cause of this behavior and what factor in the function models it?

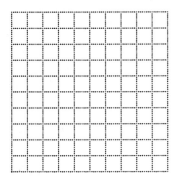

b. Find $\lim\limits_{t \to \infty} 0.75e^{-0.2t}\sin(6.2t)$.

c. Approximate the first three times that the weight passes the point of equilibrium.

d. Approximate the first three times the instantaneous velocity of the weight is zero.

2. Consider the logistics function $f(x) = \dfrac{150}{1 + 2e^{-x/4}}$.

    a. Graph the function and identify the asymptotes.

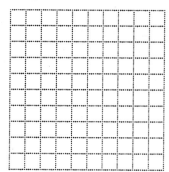

    b. Find the point on the graph where the graph is increasing at its maximum rate.

    c. Verify that the function

$$y = \frac{L}{1 + ae^{-x/b}}, \quad a \neq 0, b > 0$$

    increases at its maximum rate when $y = L/2$.

3. The following table gives the gross profit, P (in billions of dollars), for Coca-Cola Company in terms of time. (*Source:* 1992 Annual Report)

t	2	3	4	5	6	7	8	9	10	11	12
P	2.288	2.476	2.704	2.970	3.523	4.025	4.636	5.074	6.028	6.923	8.019

A model for this data is given by $P = 1.667e^{0.1275t}$ where t is time in years with $t = 0$ corresponding to 1980.

a. Plot the points and graph the model.

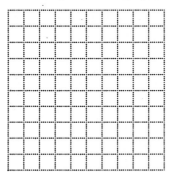

b. Add the profits recorded in the table and compare it with the values of the integrals

$$\int_2^{12} 1.667e^{0.1275t}\, dt \quad \text{and} \quad \int_{1.5}^{12.5} 1.667e^{0.1275t}\, dt.$$

State why one integral gives a better approximation of the cumulative profits.

c. Estimate how much time will elapse (after 1992) before cumulative gross profits increase by $20 billion.

This worksheet uses a 2D function grapher, a symbolic differentiation utility and a symbolic integration utility.

Name _____

Date _____

1. Consider the functions $f(x) = \left(1 + \dfrac{1}{x}\right)^x$ and $g(x) = (1 + x)^{1/x}$.

    a. Use a computer/calculator to graph the functions.

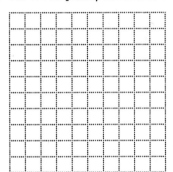 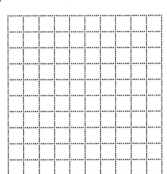

    b. Complete the following tables and estimate $\lim\limits_{x \to \infty} f(x)$ and $\lim\limits_{x \to 0+} g(x)$.

x	1	2	5	10	10^2	10^3	10^4
$f(x)$							

x	1	0.5	0.2	0.1	10^{-2}	10^{-3}	10^{-4}
$g(x)$							

c. Suppose an error was made in part **a** when entering the function f in the computer/calculator. The function entered was

$$f(x) = \left(-1 + \frac{1}{x}\right)^x.$$

Graph this function and explain why its domain is restricted.

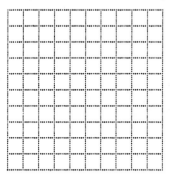

2. Two people each receive $100. One deposits the money in an account earning 8% interest compounded annually and the other deposits the money in an account earning 8% interest compounded continuously. Therefore, the respective amount in each account after t years is given by

$$A_1 = 100(1.08)^{[[t]]} \quad \text{and} \quad A_2 = 100e^{0.08t}.$$

a. Graph the functions A_1, A_2, and $A_2 - A_1$ over the interval $[0, 20]$.

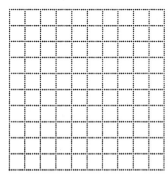

b. Which function increases at the greater rate? How can proper timing minimize the difference in the value of the accounts in the year when the money is withdrawn?

3. a. Use a computer/calculator to integrate each of the functions

$$f(t) = 5\left(\frac{4}{3}\right)^{t/2}, \quad g(t) = 5\left(\frac{2\sqrt{3}}{3}\right)^{t}, \quad \text{and} \quad h(t) = 5e^{0.143841t}$$

on the interval $[0, 10]$.

b. Graph the three functions.

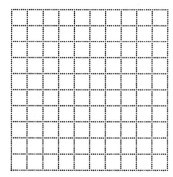

c. From the results in parts **a** and **b**, what inference can you make about the three functions? Could you make this inference based on part **a.** alone? Why or why not? Verify your inference about f and g analytically.

4. The value V of a new machine t years after it is purchased is given by

$$V(t) = 20{,}000 \left(\frac{3}{4}\right)^{t}, \quad 0 \le t \le 10.$$

a. Determine the average rate of change of the value of the machine over its 10-year lifetime.

b. Determine the instantaneous rate of change of the function when $t = 0$ and $t = 10$.

c. Determine the time when the instantaneous rate of change equals the average rate of change over the lifetime of the machine.

d. Graph the function, the secant line connecting the endpoints of the graph over the 10-year period, and the tangent line parallel to the specified secant line.

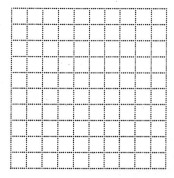

This worksheet uses a 2D function grapher,
a symbolic differentiation utility and a
symbolic integration utility.

Name _____

Date _____

**In Exercises 1 and 2, a. solve the differential equation by
separating the variables, b. use a computer/calculator to graph
the antiderivative for three different values of the constant of
integration, and c. find an equation for y that passes through the
point (2, 10).**

1. $\dfrac{dy}{dx} = 0.5y$

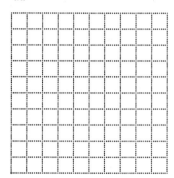

2. $\dfrac{dy}{dx} = 0.5(25 - y)$

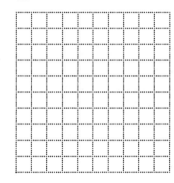

3. The following table gives the sales in millions of dollars of Merck & Company, Inc. for the years 1982–1992. (*Source:* 1992 Annual Report)

Year	1982	1983	1984	1985	1986	1987
Sales	$3063.0	$3246.1	$3559.7	$3547.5	$4128.9	$5061.3

Year	1988	1989	1990	1991	1992
Sales	$5939.5	$6550.5	$7671.5	$8602.7	$9662.5

Plot the sales versus time where S is sales in millions and t in years is time with $t = 0$ corresponding to 1990. By making careful choices for C and k and using a computer/calculator to graph

$$S = Ce^{kt},$$

find a function which fits the sales data well. Use the result to estimate the continuous percentage rate of growth in sales of the company over the given time period.

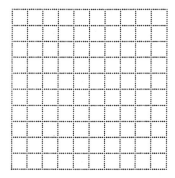

4. A brokerage firm plans to advertise a new financial service. The percentages of the target audience reached after t weeks of television advertising and newspaper advertising are approximately

$$f(t) = 90(1 - e^{-t/2}) \quad \text{and} \quad g(t) = \frac{90}{1 + 20e^{-t}},$$

respectively.

a. Use a computer/calculator to graph the functions.

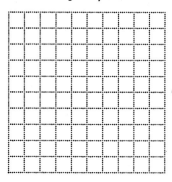

b. Determine how many weeks it will take for three-fourths of the target audience be informed for each method of advertising?

c. When will the information spread most rapidly for each of the methods?

d. Determine the limit as $t \to \infty$ for each method and interpret its meaning in the context of this exercise.

5. The value of a shipment of livestock is given by

$$V(t) = 15,000e^{1.4\sqrt{t}}$$

where t is time in days. If money earns interest continuously at 6%, then the present value of the shipment at any time t is given by

$$A(t) = V(t)e^{-0.06t}.$$

Graph the present value function and find the time when the livestock should be sold to maximize the present value function.

This worksheet uses a 2D function grapher and a symbolic differentiation utility.

Name _____

Date _____

1. Graph the functions $y = \cos x$, $y = \arccos x$, and $y = x$. Note that the graph of one function is a reflection of the other function in the line $y = x$. Give the domain and range of the inverse cosine.

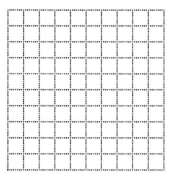

2. Graph the functions

$$f(x) = \frac{|x|}{x} \quad \text{and} \quad g(x) = \arcsin \frac{|x|}{x}.$$

Determine and state the relationship between the ranges of the functions.

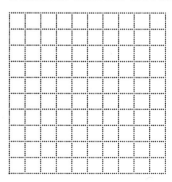

3. Use a computer/calculator to obtain the graphs of $f(x) = \tan x$ and $g(x) = \arctan(\tan x)$ on the interval $-10 \leq x \leq 10$. Explain why the graph of g is not the line $y = x$.

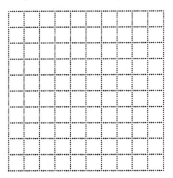

4. A television camera is mounted on a stand 2 feet high. It is positioned 15 feet behind home plate (see figure). A batter hits the ball in a path directly away from the camera modeled by the equation

$$y = -0.002x^2 + 0.577x + 3.$$

a. Write the angle of elevation θ of the camera as a function of x.

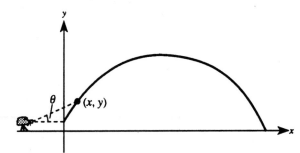

b. Graph the path of the ball and the angle of elevation function in part **a.**

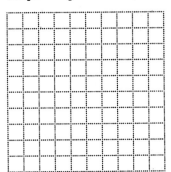 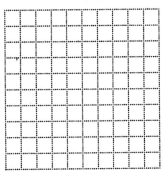

c. Find the maximum height of the ball and the maximum angle of elevation of the camera. Do the two extrema occur at the same time? Explain.

d. When must the camera operator change the angle of elevation of the camera at the fastest rate?

This worksheet uses a 2D function grapher, a symbolic differentiation utility, and a symbolic integration utility.

Name _____

Date _____

1. Use a computer/calculator to graph

$$y_1 = \sinh x, \ y_2 = \frac{e^x - e^{-x}}{2}, \ y_3 = \sinh^{-1} x, \ \text{and} \ y_4 = \ln(x + \sqrt{x^2 + 1})$$

and discuss the relationship between the four functions.

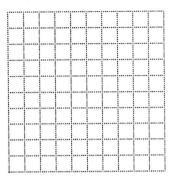

2. Consider the function $f(x) = \cosh x$.

   a. This function models the curve, called a catenary, formed by a flexible cable of uniform density and appears to be parabolic. A quadratic approximation of f is given by

$$P_2(x) = f(0) + f'(0)x + \frac{f''(0)}{2}x^2.$$

Use a computer/calculator to graph f and P_2.

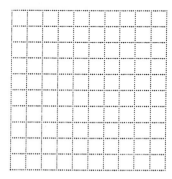

   b. It appears that the quadratic function in part **a** would better approximate the catenary if the coefficient of the second degree term were increased. Graph f and two additional quadratic functions with slightly larger coefficients of the second degree term. Describe the results.

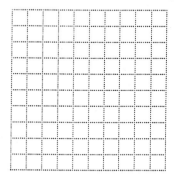

3. a. Use a computer/calculator to graph the functions $f(x) = \arctan x$ and $g(x) = \tanh x$ and their derivatives.

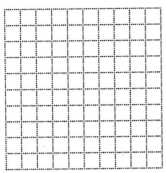

b. Determine the limits $\lim\limits_{x \to \infty} f(x)$ and $\lim\limits_{x \to \infty} g(x)$.

c. Write a short paragraph comparing the two functions.

4. Evaluate $\displaystyle\int_0^2 \frac{2x}{\sqrt{x^4 - 4x^2 + 5}}\, dx$ without the aid of a computer/calculator. (Begin by completing the square.)

5. Selected tensile strengths, S (in thousands of pounds per square inch), of nickel 200 at temperature, t (in thousands of degrees Fahrenheit), are given in the following table. (*Source:* Standard Handbook for Mechanical Engineers)

t	0.6	0.8	1	1.2	1.5	1.8
S	83	76	46	34	25	8

A model for this data is given by

$$S = 348.7\operatorname{sech} t + 89.4t - 263.2, \quad 0.6 \le t \le 1.8.$$

a. Use a computer/calculator to graph the data and the model.

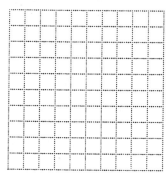

b. Determine the temperature on the specified interval at which the rate of change of tensile strength changes most rapidly with increasing temperature.

c. The tensile strength of nickel also decreases for colder temperatures. Determine the temperature at which the tensile strength maximized according to this model. (This temperature is outside the interval for which the model was determined. It is presumed for the purpose of this problem that the continuous function $S(t)$ given above models the tensile strength over a larger interval than the stated [0.6, 1.8].)

This worksheet uses a 2D function grapher, a symbolic differentiation utility, and a symbolic integration utility.

Name _____

Date _____

1. A circle of radius 2 has its center on the y-axis and is tangent to the parabola $y = x^2$ (see figure). Determine the equation of the circle and find the area of the region below the circle and above the parabola.

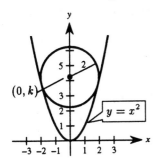

2. Sales, S (in billions of dollars), of franchised auto dealers for selected years is given in the following table. (*Source:* National Automobile Dealers Association)

Year	1983	1984	1985	1986	1987	1988	1989	1990
S	187.7	225.9	251.6	270.4	280.5	302.4	309.7	308.4

A model for this data is given by

$$S_1 = 59.2 + 50.5t - 2.5t^2 + 71.2e^{-t}, \quad 3 \le t \le 10$$

where t is time in years with $t = 0$ corresponding to 1980. For the years 1983 through 1987 the sales data is modeled by

$$S_2 = 23.8t + 130, \quad 3 \le t \le 7.$$

a. Graph the data and the two sales functions.

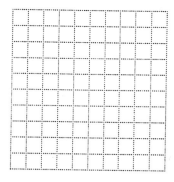

b. Note that the rate of increase of sales began to decline as the nation entered a recession. Approximate the total loss of sales revenue for the years 1987 through 1990 by extending S_2 linearly through 1990 and finding the area between S_1 and S_2.

3. Thermodynamics allows us to study ideal models for a heat engine that converts heat energy to mechanical energy. For an idealized engine, assume that the processes are pure and that gases obey ideal gas law for adiabatic expansion, $PV^\gamma = $ constant ($\gamma \approx 1.4$ for air). The work done by the system in one complete cycle in an ideal heat engine is given by the area enclosed in the cycle when illustrated on a pressure versus volume diagram. A gasoline engine is modeled by the Otto cycle (see figure). Air and gasoline are placed in the cylinder at point b. The mixture is compressed adiabatically to the point c. A spark is provided and the pressure increases very rapidly to point d. The hot gas then expands adiabatically to point a, where the combustion products are exhausted. Calculate the net work in one cycle of this engine. (Begin by finding the constant in the gas law for each of the curves and then find the area between the curves.)

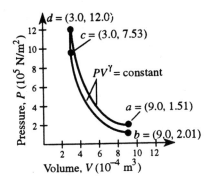

This worksheet uses a 2D function grapher and a symbolic integration utility.

Name _____

Date _____

1. Each function in parts **a–f** passes through the points $(1, 0)$ and $(0, 1)$. Graph the region bounded by the function and coordinate axes. Find the volume generated by revolving the region about the x-axis and about the y-axis.

a. $y = 1 - x^4$

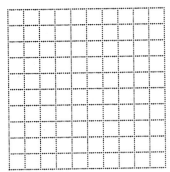

b. $y = 1 - x^3$

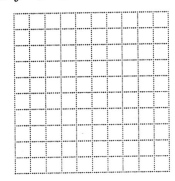

c. $y = 1 - x$

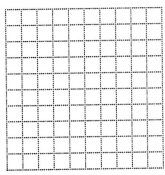

d. $y = 1 - \sqrt{x}$

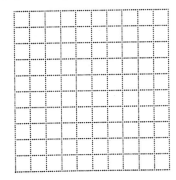

e. $y = (1 - \sqrt{x})^2$

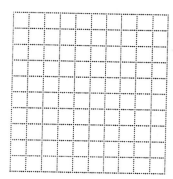

f. $y = \dfrac{1 - x}{1 + x}$

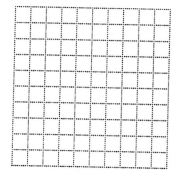

2. In some cases in Exercise 1 the two volumes calculated were equal. What characteristic of the function caused this to occur?

3. A tent has an 8-foot square base. The tent is supported by two flexible poles, the ends of which are at opposite vertices of the base (see figure). The height at the center of the tent is $4\sqrt{2}$ feet. The curve from the center of one edge of the base to the center of the opposite edge is that part of the ellipse

$$\frac{x^2}{16} + \frac{y^2}{32} = 1 \quad \text{with} \quad y \geq 0.$$

a. Find the volume of the tent.

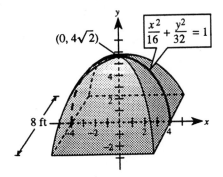

b. What is the curve formed by the flexible supporting poles?

4. A machine part is in the form of a solid of revolution (see figure). The heights (in centimeters) of a cross section are shown on the figure.

a. Use Simpson's Rule with $n = 8$ to approximate the volume obtained when that part of the solid in the xy plane between $x = 4$ and $x = 36$ is revolved about the y-axis. Add this to the volume of the central cylinder of radius 4 to obtain an approximation of the volume of the part.

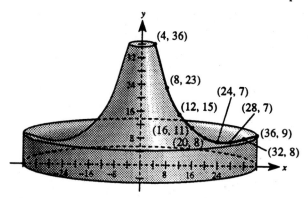

b. A model for the curved part of the measured region is

$$y = 86.68 + 3.05x - 31.22\sqrt{x}, \quad 4 \le x \le 36.$$

Use this model to approximate the volume of the part.

This worksheet uses a 2D function grapher, a symbolic differentiation utility and a symbolic integration utility.

Name _____

Date _____

Your computer/calculator may not evaluate some of the definite integrals in this laboratory. For those cases, use Simpson's Rule with $n = 20$.

1. Consider the two regions bounded by the functions $f(x) = 1 - x^2$ and $g(x) = 1 - \sqrt{x}$ and the coordinate axes on the interval $[0, \ 1]$.

a. Graph the two regions.

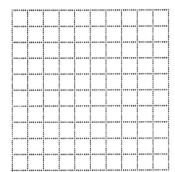 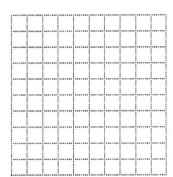

b. Find the length of the arc of the graph of f over the specified interval.

c. Find the length of the arc of the graph of g over the specified interval.

d. Suppose the enclosed region represented an area that needed to be surrounded by a fence. Consider the arc lengths as part of the fencing required to enclose the region. Determine the fractions obtained by dividing the length of each of the arcs by the area of the corresponding region. How could you use these fractions to determine which function yields more area for the amount of fencing used? Is there a still better function between the points (1, 0) and (0, 1)? If so, give the function.

e. Now revolve the given regions about the x-axis and analyze the relationship between the surface areas of the solids and the volumes of the solids. Follow the pattern in parts b–d using surface area and volume rather than arc length and area.

2. A person is holding a 20-foot rope that is tied to a boat (see figure). As the person walks along the dock, the boat travels along the tractrix given by the equation

$$y = 20 \operatorname{sech}^{-1} \frac{x}{20} - \sqrt{20^2 - x^2}.$$

Find the distance the boat moves when x decreases from $x = 20$ to $x = 1$. What is the y-coordinate of the boat when $x = 1$?

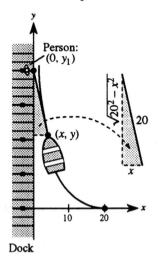

3. A machine part is in the form of a solid of revolution (see figure). The heights (in centimeters) of a cross section are shown and a model for these measurements is

$$y = 86.68 + 3.05x - 31.22\sqrt{x}, \quad 4 \le x \le 36.$$

Use this model to approximate the surface area of the solid over the given interval.

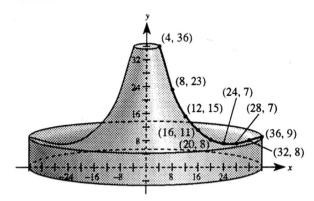

This worksheet uses a 2D function grapher
and a symbolic integration utility.

Name _____

Date _____

1. The top of an underground cavern is 1200 feet below ground level. The
   shape of the cavern is approximated by the solid of revolution formed by
   revolving the ellipse

   $$\frac{x^2}{600^2} + \frac{y^2}{200^2} = 1$$

   about its major axis (see figure). The cavern is filled with sea water which
   weighs approximately 64 lb/ft^3. Crude oil weighing approximately 54 lb/ft^3
   will be pumped into the cavity through one well head forcing the sea water
   out through another well head.

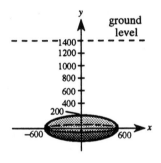

   a. Determine the storage capacity of the cavern in barrels. (One cubic foot
      holds 7.48 gallons and the volume of one barrel is 42 gallons.)

   b. Find the work done in filling the cavern with oil. (*Note:* Use the difference
      of the weights of the two liquids in calculating the work.)

2. Assume that the relationship between pressure p and volume V of a fixed mass of air is given by $pV^{1.4} = k$ where k is a constant. The initial volume of air in a one-cylinder engine is 225 cm^3 and its pressure is 1 kg/cm^2. Find the work done on the compression stroke if the air is compressed to 25 cm^3.

3. An in-ground swimming pool is 40 feet long and 20 feet wide. It is 4 feet deep at one end and 8 feet deep at the other. The bottom of the pool slopes down along a curved path (see figure).

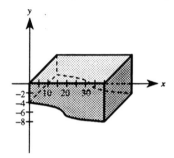

Because the owners are experiencing difficulties with the long side-walls, the design engineers recalculate the fluid force on the wall. Starting from the shallow end, the engineers measure the horizontal distance x necessary for each one-half foot change in depth y. The results are given in the following table.

x	0	9	14	17	18	19	22	27	40
y	-4	-4.5	-5	-5.5	-6	-6.5	-7	-7.5	-8

a. Use Simpson's Rule to approximate the fluid force against the 40-foot vertical wall.

b. A mathematical model for the relationship between x and y is given by

$$x = 299.614 + 26.333y + \frac{780.913}{y} + 0.016e^{-y}.$$

Use this model to approximate the fluid force against the 40-foot wall.

c. Why were the measurements made using equal incremental changes in y rather than x?

d. Approximate the number of gallons of water needed to fill the pool.

This worksheet uses a symbolic integration utility.

Name _____

Date _____

1. Find the centroid of the region shown in the figure.

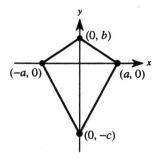

2. a. Find the centroid of the sector of a circle shown in the figure where $0 < \theta \leq \pi/2$. Write the answer in terms of r, θ, and $\sin \theta$.

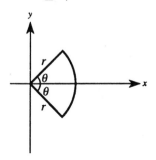

b. Find, if possible, $\lim_{\theta \to 0+} \bar{x}$.

c. Complete the following table.

θ	$\dfrac{\pi}{60}$	$\dfrac{\pi}{10}$	$\dfrac{\pi}{6}$	$\dfrac{\pi}{4}$	$\dfrac{\pi}{3}$	$\dfrac{\pi}{2}$
$\bar{x}$						

3. The cross-section of a prefabricated concrete module used in constructing a bridge consists of lines and quarter circles as shown in the accompanying figure.

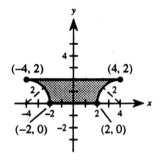

a. Find the area of the cross-section using geometric formulas.

b. Assume that the module is 10 feet long. Find the volume of concrete in the module and determine the weight of the concrete. (Concrete weighs 148 lb/ft³.)

c. Find the centroid of the cross-section.

d. Find the centroid of the cross-section if the shorter line segment is $2a$ units in length and the radius of the circular arcs is b.

This worksheet uses a 2D function grapher and a symbolic integration utility.

Name _____

Date _____

1. Consider the function $f(t) = (4 - t)e^{-t/2}$.

   a. Find $F(x) = \displaystyle\int_0^x f(t)\, dt$ without the aid of a computer/calculator. Verify your answer by differentiation.

   b. Graph $f(t)$ and $F(x)$.

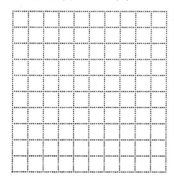

   c. Give a geometric interpretation of $F(x)$ for a particular value of x on the interval $[0,\ 4]$. Identify your answer by shading the region on the graph in part **b**.

2. Consider the indefinite integral $\int x^n \cos x \, dx$.

    a. Evaluate the integral for $n = 1$ without the aid of a computer/calculator.

    b. Use a computer/calculator to evaluate the integral for $n = 2$, $n = 3$, $n = 4$, and $n = 5$.

    c. Is there a pattern to the antiderivatives in part **b** as n increases? If so, use that pattern to find the antiderivative for the cases when $n = 6$ and $n = 7$. Use a computer/calculator to check your results.

Let $f(x)$ be a periodic function with period 2π which is approximated by

$$S_k(x) = a_0 + \sum_{n=1}^{k} (a_n \cos nx + b_n \sin nx)$$

where

$$a_0 = \frac{1}{2\pi} \int_{-\pi}^{\pi} f(x)\,dx, \quad a_n = \frac{1}{\pi} \int_{-\pi}^{\pi} f(x) \cos nx\,dx, \quad \text{and} \quad b_n = \frac{1}{\pi} \int_{-\pi}^{\pi} f(x) \sin nx\,dx.$$

In Exercises 3 and 4, a. use a computer/calculator to graph $f(x)$, through two periods and b. use a computer/calculator to find and graph the functions $S_1(x)$, $S_2(x)$, $S_3(x)$, and $S_4(x)$.

3. $f(x) = \begin{cases} -1, & -\pi < x < 0 \\ 1, & 0 < x < \pi \end{cases}$

$f(x + 2\pi) = f(x)$

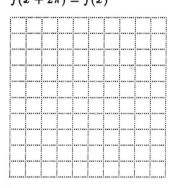

4. $f(x) = \begin{cases} x + \pi, & -\pi < x < 0 \\ \pi - x, & 0 < x < \pi \end{cases}$

$f(x + 2\pi) = f(x)$

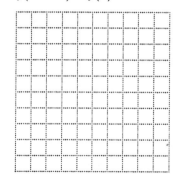

5. Identify a pattern in the results of Exercise 3 and make a conjecture about the functions $S_5(x)$ and $S_7(x)$. Test your conjecture by graphing $S_5(x)$ and $S_7(x)$ and comparing the results with the graphs in Exercise 3. Has the approximation of f improved? Explain.

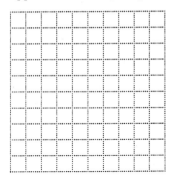

6. Identify a pattern in the results of Exercise 4 and make a conjecture about the functions $S_5(x)$ and $S_7(x)$. Test your conjecture by graphing $S_5(x)$ and $S_7(x)$ and comparing the results with the graphs in Exercise 4. Has the approximation of f improved? Explain.

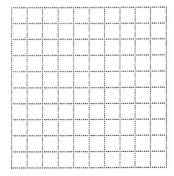

This worksheet uses a 2D function grapher and a symbolic integration utility.

Name _____

Date _____

1. Use the set of functions $\{1, \cos x, \cos 2x, \cos 3x, \ldots, \sin x, \sin 2x, \sin 3x, \ldots\}$ to answer parts a–c.

   a. Evaluate $\int_{-\pi}^{\pi} \sin^2 mx \, dx$ for two values of m ($m = 1, 2, 3, \ldots$) and make an inference about the value of the integral.

   b. Evaluate $\int_{-\pi}^{\pi} \cos^2 mx \, dx$ for two values of m ($m = 0, 1, 2, 3, \ldots$) and make an inference about the value of the integral.

c. Graph the integrand of $\displaystyle\int_{-\pi}^{\pi} \sin mx \cos nx\, dx$ for two pairs of values for m and n and make an inference about the value of the integral. Use a computer/calculator to verify your inference.

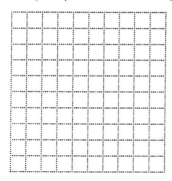

2. A spindle is formed by revolving the region bounded by the graphs of

$$y = \frac{1}{4}\left[1 + 2e^{-x/8}\sin^2\left(\frac{\pi x}{4}\right)\right], \; y = 0, \; x = 0, \text{ and } x = 8$$

about the x-axis. Determine the volume of the spindle.

3. The consumption of lumber, C (in billions of cubic feet), for selected years is given in the following table. (*Source:* U.S. Forest Service)

Year	1980	1982	1983	1984	1985	1986	1987	1988
C	6.45	5.78	6.93	7.56	7.70	8.45	8.86	8.43

A model for this data is given by

$$C = 6.44 + 0.84t - 1.70\sqrt{t} + 1.21 \sin^3\left(\frac{\pi t}{10}\right), \quad 0 \le t \le 8$$

where t is time in years with $t = 0$ corresponding to 1980.

a. Graph the data and the model.

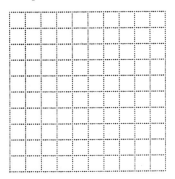

b. Use the model to approximate the average annual consumption over the given time period.

c. Use the model to determine the calendar year when lumber consumption was increasing at the greatest rate. If the model is used as a forecast tool, then determine the next calendar year when consumption will be increasing most rapidly.

This worksheet uses a 2D function grapher and a symbolic integration utility.

Name _____

Date _____

1. The force required to move a component 4 feet in a manufacturing process is given by

$$F(x) = \frac{1200x(4-x)}{\sqrt{4+x^2}}, \quad 0 \le x \le 4.$$

    a. Use a computer/calculator to determine the work done in moving one component through the distance of 4 feet.

    b. Use trigonometric substitution to rewrite the integral in part **a.** Use a computer/calculator to evaluate this integral and compare the result with that in part **a.**

2. The top of a semicircular viewing window in an aquarium is 12 feet below the surface of the water. If the viewing window is divided into three equal sectors, find the fluid force on each. Even though the areas of the sectors are equal, the fluid forces are not all equal. Explain.

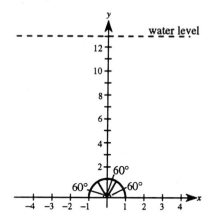

3. Consider the function $f(x) = x^2\sqrt{4 - x^2} + k$ (k is constant) on the interval $[-2, 2]$.

a. Graph the function for $k = 0$, $k = 1$, and $k = 2$.

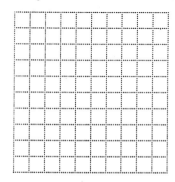

b. Find the centroid, in terms of k, of the region bounded by the graphs of $x = -2$, $x = 2$, $y = 0$, and $y = f(x)$. Complete the following table.

k	0	1	2	3
$(\bar{x}, \bar{y})$				

c. Note that the centroid is outside the region when k is "small." Find the value of k when the centroid is on the boundary of the region.

This worksheet uses a 2D function grapher, a symbolic integration utility and matrix operations.

Name _____

Date _____

1. The process of decomposing the rational function

$$f(x) = \frac{4x^3 - 3x^2 - 16x - 13}{(x-2)(x-3)(x^2+1)}$$

into a sum of partial fractions begins as follows:

$$\frac{4x^3 - 3x^2 - 16x - 13}{(x-2)(x-3)(x^2+1)}$$

$$= \frac{A}{x-2} + \frac{B}{x-3} + \frac{Cx+D}{x^2+1}$$

$$= \frac{(A+B+C)x^3 + (-3A - 2B - 5C + D)x^2 + (A + B + 6C - 5D)x + (-3A - 2B + 6D)}{(x-2)(x-3)(x^2+1)}.$$

a. Equate the coefficients of like terms of the numerators and use a computer/calculator to solve the resulting system of equations.
(*Note:* Determine if your computer/calculator has the capability of finding the partial fraction decomposition of a rational function directly. If so, use that capability to verify the results of solving the system of equations.)

b. Use the result in part **a** to evaluate $\displaystyle\int \frac{4x^3 - 3x^2 - 16x - 13}{(x-2)(x-3)(x^2+1)}$ wihout the aid of a symbolic integration utility.

c. Use a computer/calculator to evaluate the integral in part **b.**

In Exercises 2 and 3, use a computer/calculator to find the partial fraction decomposition of the integrand and evaluate the integral.

2. $\displaystyle\int \frac{4(x^2 + 2x + 4)}{(x+2)^2(2-x)}\, dx$

3. $\displaystyle\int \frac{4x^3 - 37x^2 + 113x - 95}{2(x-4)^2(x^2+x+1)}\, dx$

4. The sales of three-quarter inch particleboard, S (in billions of square feet), for selected years is given in the following table. (*Source:* U.S. Department of Commerce)

Year	1980	1983	1984	1985	1986	1987	1988	1989	1990
S	2.95	3.01	3.20	3.33	3.60	3.71	3.83	3.86	3.81

A model for this data is given by

$$S = \frac{2.949 - 0.706t + 0.066t^2}{1 - 0.237t + 0.020t^2}, \quad 0 \le t \le 10$$

where t is time in years with $t = 0$ corresponding to 1980.

a. Graph the data and the model.

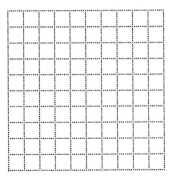

b. Use the model to approximate the total sales of particleboard from 1980 through 1990 and the average annual sales over the given time period.

c. Use the model to determine the calendar year when sales were increasing at the greatest rate.

This worksheet uses a 2D function grapher and a symbolic integration utility.

Name _____

Date _____

In Exercises 1–4, use a computer/calculator to determine the convergence or divergence of the improper integral. Give the value of the integral if it converges.

1. $\displaystyle\int_0^2 \frac{x}{\sqrt{16 - x^4}}\, dx$

2. $\displaystyle\int_0^1 x^2 \ln x\, dx$

3. $\displaystyle\int_0^\infty \frac{x}{(1 + x^2)^2}\, dx$

4. $\displaystyle\int_0^\infty \frac{10}{\sqrt{4x + 25}}\, dx$

5. a. Use a computer/calculator to graph the functions

$$f(x) = \frac{1}{x^2} \quad \text{and} \quad g(x) = \frac{\cos^2 x}{x^2}.$$

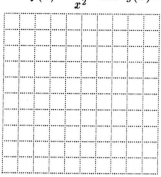

b. Determine the convergence or divergence of the improper integral

$$\int_1^\infty \frac{1}{x^2}\, dx.$$

c. Although you cannot determine the antiderivative of $g(x)$, use the results in parts **a** and **b** to determine the convergence of divergence of

$$\int_1^\infty g(x)\, dx.$$

Give reasons for your answer.

A nonnegative function f is called a **probability density function** if

$$\int_{-\infty}^{\infty} f(t)\,dt = 1.$$

The **probability** that x lies between a and b is given by

$$P(a \le x \le b) = \int_{a}^{b} f(t)\,dt.$$

In Exercises 6–8, use the density function for the gamma distribution given by

$$f(t) = \begin{cases} \dfrac{1}{\beta^{\alpha}\Gamma(\alpha)} t^{\alpha-1} e^{-t/\beta}, & t > 0 \\ 0, & t \le 0 \end{cases}$$

where $\alpha > 0$, $\beta > 0$, and $\Gamma(\alpha) = \displaystyle\int_{0}^{\infty} t^{\alpha-1} e^{-t}\,dt$.

6. Use a computer/calculator to graph the density function for
   a. $\alpha = 1$, $\beta = 1$, **b.** $\alpha = 2$, $\beta = 1$, **c.** $\alpha = 4$, $\beta = 1$, and **d.** $\alpha = 2$, $\beta = 2$.

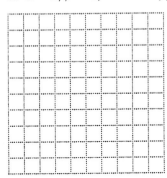

7. Use a computer/calculator to verify that each of the functions in Exercise 6 is a density function. [*Note:* It is only necessary to integrate over the interval $[0, \infty)$.]

8. The daily demand for water (in millions of liters) in a certain city is approximated by a gamma distribution with $\alpha = 3$ and $\beta = 2$.

    a. Find the probability that the demand will be between 3 and 5 million liters on a given day.

    b. Find the probability that demand will exceed 10 million liters on a specific day.

This worksheet uses a 2D function grapher.

Name _____

Date _____

In Exercises 1–4, a. **find the sum of the series, b. use a computer/ calculator to evaluate the first 10 terms of the sequence of partial sums S_n, and c. graph the horizontal line representing the sum of the series and the 10 points given by (n, S_n).**

1. $\displaystyle\sum_{n=0}^{\infty} \frac{9}{4}\left(\frac{1}{4}\right)^n$

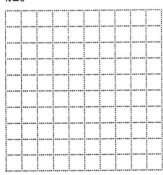

2. $\displaystyle\sum_{n=0}^{\infty} \left(\frac{2}{3}\right)^n$

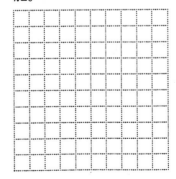

3. $\displaystyle\sum_{n=0}^{\infty} \frac{15}{4}\left(-\frac{1}{4}\right)^n$

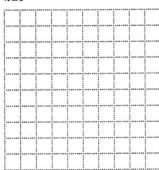

4. $\displaystyle\sum_{n=0}^{\infty} \frac{17}{3}\left(-\frac{8}{9}\right)^n$

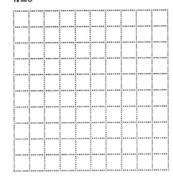

5. Use the graphs of Exercises 1–4 to describe how the common ratio of a geometric series influences the sequence of partial sums as its terms approach the sum of the series. In particular, discuss the effect of the magnitude and sign of r.

6. Consider the geometric series $1 - \dfrac{x}{3} + \dfrac{x^2}{9} - \dfrac{x^3}{27} + \cdots$.

  a. What is the common ratio of the series and for what values of x will the series converge? Determine the function f representing the sum of the series.

  b. Graph the sum, $f(x)$, of the series. Graph the line given by the first 2 terms of the series. Identify the line. Graph the sixth degree polynomial given by the first 7 terms of the series.

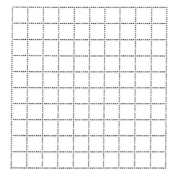

7. Each month, P dollars of an employee's paycheck is invested in a retirement account. These deposits are made each month for t years and the account earns interest at the annual percentage rate r. If the interest is compounded monthly, the amount A in the account at the end of t years is

$$A_t = P + P\left(1 + \frac{r}{12}\right) + \cdots + P\left(1 + \frac{r}{12}\right)^{12t-1}.$$

Suppose $100 is deposited at the end of each month for 30 years into an account earning $6\frac{1}{2}\%$ compounded monthly.

a. Use a computer/calculator to determine the set of ordered pairs $\{(1, A_1), (2, A_2), \ldots, (30, A_{30})\}$. Plot these points. (These ordered pairs give the amount in the account at the end of each year for the 30 years.)

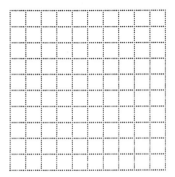

b. If the points in the graph in part **a** were connected with a smooth curve, would the curve be concave up or concave down? What information does this give about the rate of growth of the account? Does the sequence of the amounts A_t converge or diverge?

This worksheet uses a 2D function grapher and a symbolic integration utility.

Name _____

Date _____

1. a. Use a computer/calculator to find the sum of the first 9 terms of the series

$$\sum_{n=1}^{\infty} \frac{9}{n^{3/2}}.$$

b. Graph the function $f(x) = 9/x^{3/2}$ and shade the rectangles of width 1 representing the Riemann sum which equals the partial sum in part **a.**

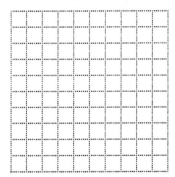

2. Use a computer/calculator to generate the set of ordered pairs $\{(1, S_1), (2, S_2), \ldots, (50, S_{50})\}$ where S_i is sum of the first i terms of the harmonic series.

   a. Use a computer/calculator to plot the 50 points and zoom out sufficiently far so all points can be seen.

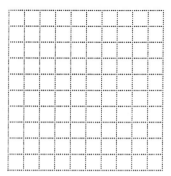

   b. Even though the graph in part **a** consists of discrete points, they are close enough to appear to be a continuous curve. Identify the function that approximates the points and graph it on the coordinate system in part **a**. Use the graph to make an inference about the convergence or divergence of the harmonic series.

3. Consider the three convergent p-series

$$\sum_{n=1}^{\infty} \frac{1}{n^2}, \quad \sum_{n=1}^{\infty} \frac{1}{n^3}, \quad \text{and} \quad \sum_{n=1}^{\infty} \frac{1}{n^4}.$$

a. For each series, use a computer/calculator to evaluate the first 50 terms of the sequence of partial sums S_n, and for each, plot the 50 points given by (n, S_n).

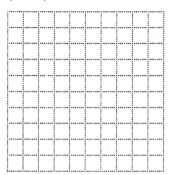

b. The remainder (error) R_{50} in using the first 50 terms of a p-series to approximate the sum of the series is bounded by

$$0 \le R_{50} \le \int_{50}^{\infty} \frac{1}{x^p} \, dx.$$

Compute the bounds on the error for the three p-series of this exercise.

c. Use the results of parts **a** and **b** to describe the relationship between the magnitudes of the terms of a series and the rate at which it converges.

4. Find the smallest N so that the remainder $R_N \leq 0.0001$ for the series

$$\sum_{n=1}^{\infty} \frac{2n}{n^4 + 1} \quad \text{where} \quad 0 \leq R_N \leq \int_{N}^{\infty} \frac{2x}{x^4 + 1}\, dx.$$

This worksheet uses a 2D function grapher.   Name _____

                                                Date _____

1. a. Determine the convergence or divergence of the series

$$\sum_{n=1}^{\infty} \frac{1}{n^2}, \ \sum_{n=1}^{\infty} \frac{1}{n^2+3}, \ \text{and} \ \sum_{n=1}^{\infty} \frac{1}{n\sqrt{n^2+3}}.$$

b. For each series, use a computer/calculator to evaluate the first 50 terms of the sequence of partial sums S_n, and for each, plot the 50 points given by (n, S_n).

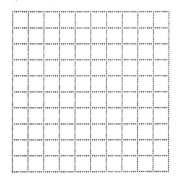

c. Though the series converge to different sums, use the graph to compare the rates at which they converge. Why is this true?

d. Repeat part **b** for the series

$$\sum_{n=6}^{\infty} \frac{1}{n^2}, \ \sum_{n=6}^{\infty} \frac{1}{n^2+3} \ \text{ and } \ \sum_{n=6}^{\infty} \frac{1}{n\sqrt{n^2+3}}.$$

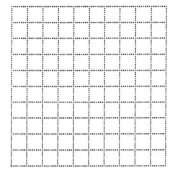

e. Does deleting the first finite number of terms of a series change its convergence or divergence? How does the sum change? Explain.

2. Consider the series $\displaystyle\sum_{n=1}^{\infty} \frac{4(-1)^{n-1}}{2n-1} = \pi$ and $\displaystyle\sum_{n=1}^{\infty} \frac{6}{\pi n^2} = \pi$.

    a. Use a computer/calculator to evaluate the first 50 terms of each series, and for each, plot the 50 points given by (n, a_n).

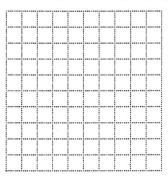

    b. For each series, use a computer/calculator to evaluate the first 50 terms of the sequence of partial sums S_n, and for each, plot the 50 points given by (n, S_n).

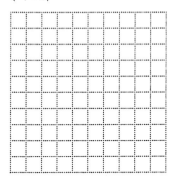

    c. Describe and give reasons for the difference in the way the sequence of partial sums of the two series approaches their sum.

d. Determine the series in which the magnitude of the terms approaches 0 at the faster rate. Why do you think the sequence of partial sums of this series doesn't approach π at a significantly faster rate?

e. Find the number of terms necessary to approximate the sum of each series with an error less than 0.0001.

This worksheet uses a 2D function grapher and a symbolic differentiation utility.

Name _____

Date _____

In Exercises 1–4, use a computer/calculator to generate the coefficients of the Taylor polynomial of degree n centered at c. Use the coefficients to write the specified polynomial. Graph the function and the polynomial, and use the graph to give an interval in which the polynomial appears to be a reasonable approximation of the function.

1. $f(x) = \ln(x + 1)$, $n = 5$, $c = 0$

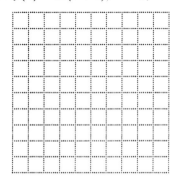

2. $f(x) = \sin^3 x$, $n = 5$, $c = 0$

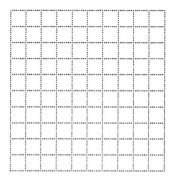

3. $f(x) = \cos x$, $n = 5$, $c = \dfrac{\pi}{2}$

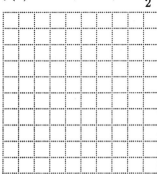

4. $f(x) = x^2 e^x$, $n = 3$, $c = -2$

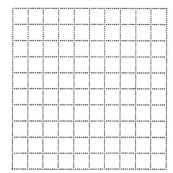

5. a. Find the Maclaurin polynomial P_6 for $f(x) = \cos^2 x$.

b. Graph f and P_6.

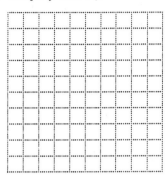

c. Using the results of parts **a** and **b**, complete the following table.

x	0	0.5	1	1.5	2	2.5	3
$f(x)$							
$P_6(x)$							
$f(x) - P_6(x)$							

d. Using the work you have done in this lab, write a short paragraph describing where a Taylor polynomial agrees with the function it approximates and what happens to its accuracy as you move away from that point.

6. Determine the degree of the Maclaurin polynomial for $f(x) = \arctan x$ so that $f(\frac{1}{2})$ can be approximated with error less than 0.0005. (Use a computer/calculator to find the required derivatives.)

This worksheet uses a 2D function grapher and a symbolic differentiation utility.

Name _____

Date _____

1. Consider the function $g(x) = \sum_{n=1}^{\infty} \dfrac{x^{n-1}}{3^n}$.

    a. Find the interval of convergence of the series.

    b. For each of the series $g(1)$, $g(2)$, and $g(2.9)$, use a computer/calculator to evaluate the first 50 terms of the sequence of partial sums S_n, and for each, plot the 50 points given by (n, S_n).

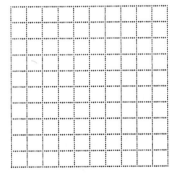

c. For each series $g(-1)$, $g(-2)$, and $g(-2.9)$, use a computer/calculator to evaluate the first 50 terms of the sequence of partial sums S_n, and for each, plot the 50 points given by (n, S_n).

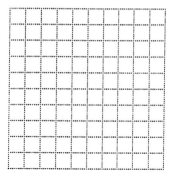

d. Describe the rate of convergence of the sequence of partial sums as the series is evaluated at values of x near the endpoints of the interval of convergence.

e. Use a computer/calculator to evaluate the first 50 terms of the sequence of partial sums S_n for the series $\displaystyle\sum_{n=1}^{\infty} \frac{x^{n-1}}{3^n}$ when $x = 3.1$. Plot the 50 points given by (n, S_n). Explain why this graph is different than those in parts b and c. Why is it meaningless to say a power series represents a function for values of x outside the interval of convergence?

2. Consider the function $f(x) = \dfrac{5}{x - 3}$.

   a. Find the power series centered at $x = 4$ for the function and determine its interval of convergence.

   b. Find the power series centered at $x = 6$ for the function and determine its interval of convergence.

   c. Graph f and the two fourth-degree polynomials obtained from the power series in parts **a** and **b**.

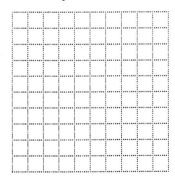

   d. Use the graphs in part **c** to identify the interval on which each polynomial gives reasonable approximations to f. Since the polynomials have the same degree, does this imply that the length of the intervals are the same?

3. a. Without the aid of a computer/calculator, find the power series centered at $x = 0$ for the function

$$f(x) = \frac{\ln(x^2 + 1)}{x^2}.$$

Find the series without the aid of a computer/calculator.

b. Graph f and the eighth-degree polynomial $P_8(x)$ obtained from the power series in part **a.**

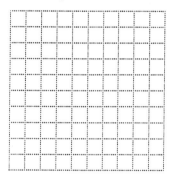

c. Complete the following table where

$$F(x) = \int_0^x \frac{\ln(t^2 + 1)}{t^2} \, dt \quad \text{and} \quad G(x) = \int_0^x P_8(t) \, dt.$$

x	0.25	0.5	0.75	1	1.5	2
$F(x)$						
$G(x)$						

d. State the relationship between the graphs in part **b** and the table in part **c.**

4. The voltage V at position x is approximated by

$$V = 12 \ln \frac{1+x}{1-x}.$$

a. Identify the domain of the function.

b. Use a computer/calculator to determine the power series centered at $x = 0$ of the voltage function.

c. Combine the power series for $y = \ln(1+x)$ and $y = \ln(1-x)$, to obtain the series for the voltage function. Compare the result with part **b.**

5. Consider the function $f(x) = \dfrac{\sin^2 x}{x}$.

    a. Use a computer/calculator to find and graph f and the seventh-degree Maclaurin polynomial P_7.

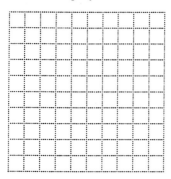

    b. Find (if it exists) $\lim\limits_{x \to 0} f(x)$ using **a.** L'Hôpital's Rule and **b.** the Maclaurin series.

    c. Use a Maclaurin polynomial to approximate the definite integral

$$\int_0^1 \frac{\sin^2 x}{x}\, dx$$

    with an error of less than 0.0001.

6. Find the fifth-degree Maclaurin polynomial P_5 of the function

$$f(x) = e^{-x/2} \cos x.$$

Graph f and P_5. Use each to approximate the maximum value of the function on the interval $[-1, 1]$.

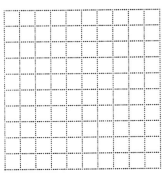

This worksheet uses a 2D function grapher and a symbolic integration utility.

Name _____

Date _____

1. a. Find the quadratic function $f(x) = ax^2 + bx + c$ whose graph passes through the points $(-3, 5)$, $(3, -7)$, and $(2, -\frac{20}{3})$. (*Hint:* Substituting the solution points into the function creates a linear system of equations. Use a computer/calculator to solve the system.)

    b. Graph the quadratic function passing through the given points identifying the vertex, focus, and directrix.

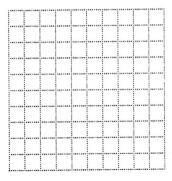

2. Consider the quadratic function $f(x) = ax^2 + bx + c$ where $a = \frac{1}{2}$, $c = 2$, and b is allowed to vary.

a. Graph the function for the following values of b : 0, ±1, ±2, ±3.

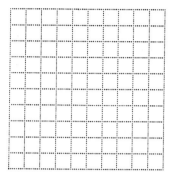

b. Connect the vertices of the parabolas graphed in part **a** with a smooth curve. Make a conjecture about the curve and find its equation. Check your conjecture by graphing the equation on the coordinate system in part **a.**

3. The distance between the supporting towers of the Golden Gate Bridge is 4200 feet and the height of the towers is 520 feet (see figure). Find an equation of one of the main suspension cables if it is a parabola with its vertex 6 feet above the road at the center of the bridge. Approximate the length of the cable.

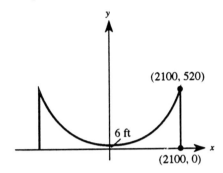

4. A storage shed for rock salt (for melting ice on roads) has the shape of a solid of revolution formed by revolving a parabola about the y-axis. The height of the shed is 27 feet and the ground-level diameter is 36 feet.

   a. Find an equation of the parabolic cross-section of the building shown in the accompanying figure.

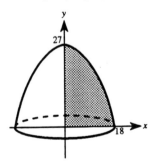

   b. Find the volume of the building.

c. Approximate the number of square feet of material needed to cover the roof of the building. (In buying shingles, this area must be reduced by the size of the doorway into the building.)

This worksheet uses a 2D function grapher and a symbolic integration utility.

Name _____

Date _____

1. a. Show that the standard form of an ellipse centered at the origin and with horizontal major axis can be written in the form

$$\frac{x^2}{a^2} + \frac{y^2}{a^2(1 - e^2)} = 1$$

where $e = c/a$ is the eccentricity of the ellipse.

b. Select an arbitrary value for a and use a computer/calculator to graph the ellipses when $e = 0.1$, $e = 0.5$, and $e = 0.9$. Label each ellipse with its eccentricity.

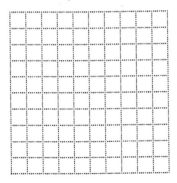

c. Describe the effect of eccentricity on the graph of an ellipse. How does the position of the foci change relative to the center and the vertices when the eccentricity is changed?

2. A rubber noise suppression bushing is formed by revolving the ellipse

$$\frac{x^2}{4} + \frac{4y^2}{9} = 1$$

about its minor axis. Find the volume of rubber in the bushing if there is a one-half inch diameter hole centered on and parallel to the axis of revolution.

3. Find the centroid of the first quadrant plane region bounded by the graph

$$\frac{x^2}{a^2} + \frac{y^2}{b^2} = 1.$$

4. The pedals of a bicycle drive a chainwheel which drives a smaller sprocket wheel on the rear axle. Many chainwheels are circular. Some, however, are slightly elliptical, which tends to make pedaling easier. The front chainwheel on the bicycle in the accompanying figure is 8 inches at its widest point and $7\frac{1}{2}$ inches at its narrowest point. The rear sprocket wheel is circular and in one of its speeds its diameter is $3\frac{1}{2}$ inches.

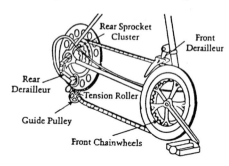

a. Use the Simpson's Rule with $n = 20$ and the elliptic integral to approximate the circumference of the chainwheel.

b. For each revolution of the chainwheel, approximate the number of revolutions of the rear wheel of the bicycle. How far will the bicycle move if the diameter of the rear wheel is 26 inches?

9.3 Hyperbolas

This worksheet uses a 2D function grapher,
a symbolic differentation utility and a
symbolic integration utility.

Name _____

Date _____

1. a. Show that the standard form of a hyperbola centered at the origin and with horizontal transverse axis can be written in the form

$$\frac{x^2}{a^2} - \frac{y^2}{a^2(e^2 - 1)} = 1$$

where $e = c/a$ is the eccentricity of the hyperbola.

b. Select an arbitrary value for a and use a computer/calculator to graph the ellipses when $e = 1.1$, $e = 1.2$, $e = 1.5$, and $e = 2$. Label each hyperbola with its eccentricity.

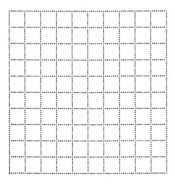

c. Describe the effect of the eccentricity on the graph of a hyperbola. How does the position of the foci change relative to the center and the vertices when the eccentricity is changed?

2. Consider the hyperbola $y^2 - x^2 = 1$ and the ellipse $\dfrac{x^2}{2} + \dfrac{y^2}{4} = 1$.

    a. Graph these conics and determine the points of intersection.

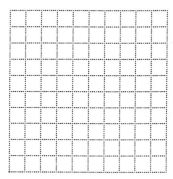

    b. Find the area of the region between the branches of the hyperbola and inside the ellipse.

3. If $a > b$ in $x^2/a^2 - y^2/b^2 = 1$, then the set of points of intersection of perpendicular tangents to the hyperbola is a circle centered at the origin. Consider the hyperbola

$$\frac{x^2}{4} - \frac{y^2}{1} = 1.$$

    a. Find two sets of perpendicular tangent lines to the hyperbola; one set for each branch.

b. Find the points of intersection of the sets of perpendicular tangent lines in part **a**, and verify that they are equidistant from the origin.

c. Write an equation of the circle centered at the origin passing through the points of intersection in part **b**.

d. Use the results of this exercise to graph the hyperbola, the sets of perpendicular tangent lines, and the circle containing the points of intersection.

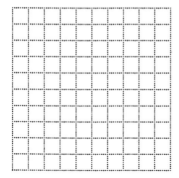

e. Sketch two more sets of tangent lines to the hyperbola that intersect on the circle. Determine whether they appear perpendicular.

This worksheet uses a 2D function grapher with solve features and a symbolic differentiation utility.

Name _____

Date _____

1. Use a computer/calculator to graph the second-degree equation

$$2x^2 + Bxy + 2y^2 - x + 2y - 5 = 0$$

for the specified values of B. (*Note:* It may be necessary to solve for y and graph the two resulting equations.)

a. $B = \frac{1}{2}$, $B = 2$, $B = 0$

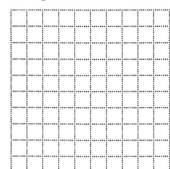

b. $B = 4$, $B = 5$, $B = 20$

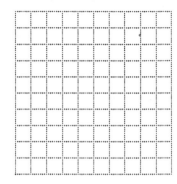

2. Use implicit differentiation to find dy/dx for the second degree equation

$$4x^2 - 4xy + y^2 - 6x + 10y - 10 = 0$$

and find an equation of each tangent line to the graph of the quadratic at its y-intercepts.

In Exercises 3 and 4, a. use a computer/calculator to graph
the conic, b. determine the angle θ through which the axes are
rotated, and c. use a computer/calculator to eliminate the xy-term
by making the substitutions

$$x = u \cos \theta - v \sin \theta$$
$$y = u \sin \theta + v \cos \theta$$

in the given equation and simplifying.

3. $x^2 + 2xy - y^2 + 3x - 5y - 2 = 0$

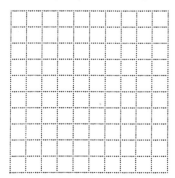

4. $2x^2 - 2xy + y^2 + x - 4y = 0$

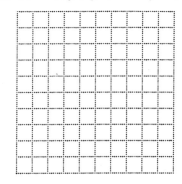

10.1 Plane Curves and Parametric Equations

This worksheet uses a 2D parametric grapher.

Name _____

Date _____

1. Use a computer/calculator to complete the table and graph the curves represented by the sets of parametric equations. Write the corresponding rectangular equation by eliminating the parameter.

a. $x = \sin \theta$

$y = 2 \cos \theta$

θ	0	$\dfrac{\pi}{4}$	$\dfrac{\pi}{2}$	$\dfrac{3\pi}{4}$	π	$\dfrac{5\pi}{4}$	$\dfrac{3\pi}{2}$	$\dfrac{7\pi}{4}$	2π
x									
y									

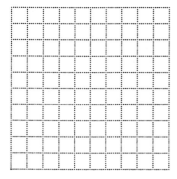

b. $x = \dfrac{1 - t^2}{1 + t^2}$

$y = \dfrac{4t}{1 + t^2}$

t	-10	-1	$-\dfrac{1}{2}$	$-\dfrac{1}{10}$	0	$\dfrac{1}{10}$	$\dfrac{1}{2}$	1	10
x									
y									

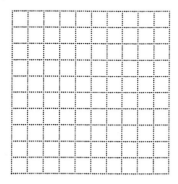

2. Use the results of Exercise **1** to describe any differences in the curves represented by the two sets of parametric equations. Are the graphs the same? Are the orientations the same? Are the curves smooth? Why does it appear that the graph in part **b** does not close at $(-1, 0)$?

3. Graph the curve represented by the parametric equations

$$x = \arcsin \frac{t}{2} \quad \text{and} \quad y = -2\ln(4 - t^2).$$

Give the interval of greatest length for t. What are the corresponding intervals for x and y?

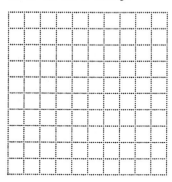

In Exercises 4–6, use the parametric equations $H(A, B)$ given by

$$x = (A - B)\cos t + B\cos\left(\frac{A - B}{B}\right)t \quad \text{and}$$

$$y = (A - B)\sin t - B\cos\left(\frac{A - B}{B}\right)t.$$

4. Use a computer/calculator to graph the hypocycloids $H(3, 1)$, $H(4, 1)$, and $H(5, 1)$. Make a conjecture about the curve given by $H(6, 1)$.

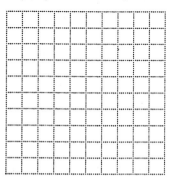

5. Graph the curves given by $H(5, 1)$ and $H(5, 4)$. For each case find the interval for t of minimum length which generates the entire curve.

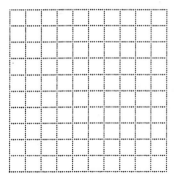

6. Graph the curves given by $H(2, 3)$ and $H(3, 4)$. Determine where each curve is smooth.

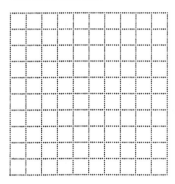

7. The path of a projectile launched at an angle θ with the horizontal, h feet above the ground level and with initial velocity v_0 feet per second, is modeled by the parametric equations

$$x = (v_0 \cos \theta)t \quad \text{and} \quad y = h + (v_0 \sin \theta)t - 16t^2.$$

A ball is thrown at an angle of 32° with the horizontal and from a height of 5 feet. The initial velocity is 70 feet per second. Graph the path of the ball. From the graph approximate the maximum height and range of the ball.

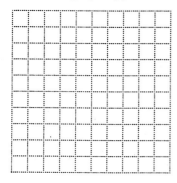

This worksheet uses a 2D parametric grapher, a symbolic differentiation utility, and a symbolic integration utility.

Name _____

Date _____

1. Consider the parametric equations given by

$$x = 3\cos\frac{t}{3} - \cos t \quad \text{and} \quad y = 3\sin\frac{t}{3} - \sin t.$$

a. Graph the curve represented by the parametric equations.

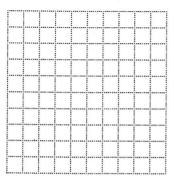

b. Find an equation of the tangent line to the curve at the point where $t = \pi/2$.

c. Find all points of horizontal and vertical tangency.

d. Use Simpson's Rule with $n = 20$ to approximate the length of the arc in the first quadrant.

2. The path of a projectile is modeled by the parametric equations

$$x = (110 \cos 25°)t \quad \text{and} \quad y = (110 \sin 25°)t - 16t^2$$

where x and y are measured in feet. Use a computer/calculator to perform the following.

a. Graph the path of the projectile and use calculus to determine its maximum height.

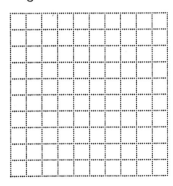

b. Use Simpson's Rule with $n = 20$ to approximate the arc length of the path (the total distance traveled by the projectile).

3. One arch of the cycloid with parametric equations $x = a(\theta - \sin \theta)$ and $y = a(1 - \cos \theta)$ is revolved about the x-axis. Find the surface area of the solid of revolution.

4. Consider the two sets of parametric equations given by

$$x = a \sin t \quad \text{and} \quad x = a \sinh t.$$
$$y = a \cos t \qquad\qquad y = a \cosh t.$$

a. Select a particular value for a and graph the curve represented by each set of parametric equations. Eliminate the parameter from each set of equations and identify the curves.

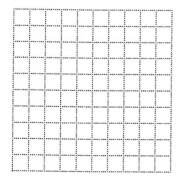
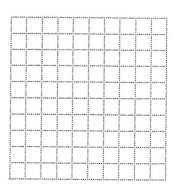

b. There is an analogy between the trigonometric functions and the hyperbolic functions through area. If A is the area of the shaded regions in each of the accompanying figures, show that $A = a^2 t_0$. (*Note:* If y is a continuous function of x on the interval $a \leq x \leq b$, where $x = f(t)$ and $y = g(t)$, then

$$\int_a^b y \, dx = \int_{t_1}^{t_2} g(t) |f'(t)| \, dt,$$

where $f(t_1) = a$, $f(t_2) = b$, and both g and f' are continuous on $[t_1, t_2]$.)

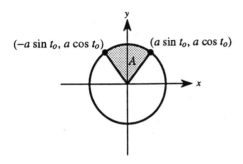

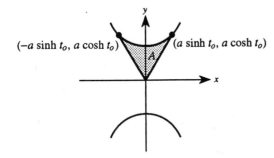

This worksheet uses a 2D polar grapher and a symbolic differentiation utility.

Name _____

Date _____

If necessary for your graphing utility, you can graph the polar function $r = f(\theta)$ by graphing the parametric equations $x = f(\theta)\cos\theta$ and $y = f(\theta)\sin\theta$.

In Exercises 1–4, use a computer/calculator to graph the polar equation. Find an interval for θ over which the graph is traced only once.

1. $r = 5\cos(3\theta)$

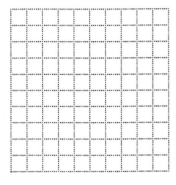

2. $r = 4\sin\left(\dfrac{6\theta}{5}\right)$

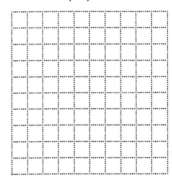

3. $r = 4\cos(2\theta)\sec\theta$

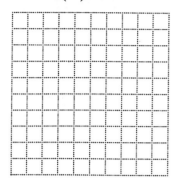

4. $r^2 = 16\cos(2\theta)$

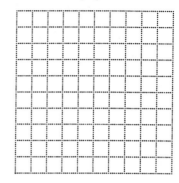

5. Graph the polar equation $r = 1 + 3\cos\theta$ and its tangents at the pole.

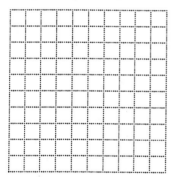

6. Consider the polar equation $r = 2\left(e^{-4\cos^2\theta} + e^{-4\sin^2\theta}\right)$. Graph the equation and the equations which result in a 30° clockwise and counterclockwise rotation of the graph. List the polar equations which yield the specified rotations.

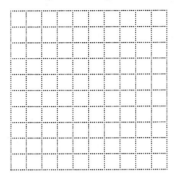

7. Consider the rectangular equation $(x^2 + y^2)^2 = ax^2 y$.

    a. Select a value for a and attempt to graph the equation using a computer/calculator. Don't be surprised if it is not possible. Make the substitutions $x = r \cos \theta$ and $y = r \sin \theta$. Use a computer/calculator to simplify the result and solve for r to obtain a polar equation of the curve.

    b. Let $a = 6$ and graph the polar equation for the curve.

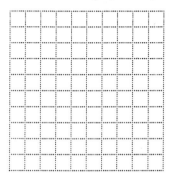

    c. Find the dy/dx and all points of vertical and horizontal tangency. Use a computer/calculator to add short line segments for the tangents to the curve at these points. (Write parametric equations whose graphs show the required tangent lines with length 1 unit.)

*This worksheet uses a 2D polar grapher,
a symbolic differentiation utility and a
symbolic integraiton utility.*

Name _____

Date _____

*If necessary for your graphing utility, you can graph the polar function
$r = f(\theta)$ by graphing the parametric equations $x = f(\theta)\cos\theta$ and
$y = f(\theta)\sin\theta$.*

1. Consider the polar equations $r = 4\sin\theta$ and $r = 2(1 + 4\cos\theta)$.

    a. Use a computer/calculator to graph the polar equations and use the graph
to approximate the coordinates of the points of intersection.

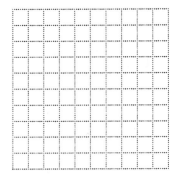

    b. Use a computer/calculator to solve the equations simultaneously in an
attempt to locate the exact coordinates of the points of intersection.
Why is the number of points different than what is shown in the graph?

c. Since (r, θ) and $(-r, \theta + \pi)$ represent the same point, replace r by $-r$ and θ by $\theta + \pi$ in **one** of the equations, and solve the equations simultaneously again. If you still did not obtain an additional point of intersection, make the replacements for r and θ in the other equation and repeat the process.

2. Consider the polar equations $r = 4 \sin \theta$ and $r = 2(2 - \sin^2 \theta)$.

    a. Use a computer/calculator to graph the polar equations and find the points of intersection.

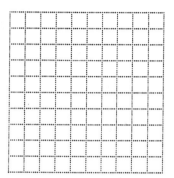

    b. Use a computer/calculator to find the area of the common interior of the two graphs.

    c. Use Simpson's Rule with $n = 20$ to approximate the circumference of $r = 2(2 - \sin^2 \theta)$.

3. Graph the surface formed by revolving the curve given by the polar equation $r = e^{-\theta/2}$, $(0 \leq \theta \leq \pi)$, about the polar axis. Find its surface area.

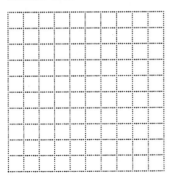

This worksheet uses a 2D polar grapher,   Name _____
a symbolic differentiation utility and a
symbolic integration utility.   Date _____

If necessary for your graphing utility, you can graph the polar function
$r = f(\theta)$ by graphing the parametric equations $x = f(\theta) \cos \theta$ and
$y = f(\theta) \sin \theta$.

1. a. Use a computer/calculator to graph the polar equation

$$r = \frac{2}{1 + e \cos \theta}$$

for the specified values of e, the eccentricity.

$e = 0.1$ $e = 0.75$ $e = 0.9$

$e = 1$ $e = 1.1$ $e = 2$

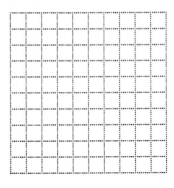 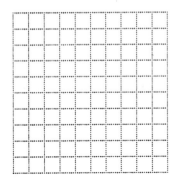 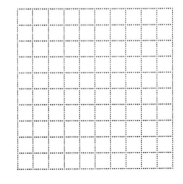

b. Describe how the graphs of the polar equations

$$r = \frac{2}{1 - 0.75 \cos \theta}, \quad r = \frac{2}{1 + 0.75 \sin \theta}, \quad \text{and} \quad r = \frac{2}{1 + 0.75 \cos(\theta - \pi/6)}$$

differ from the graph of

$$r = \frac{2}{1 + 0.75 \cos \theta}.$$

Show the results graphically.

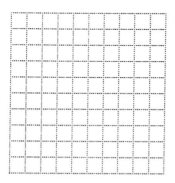 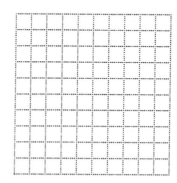 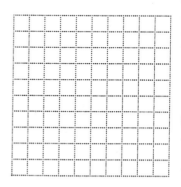

2. The planets travel in elliptical orbits with the sun as a focus. Assume that the focus is at the pole, the major axis lies on the polar axis, and the length of the major axis is $2a$ (see figure). The polar equation of the orbit is given by

$$r = \frac{(1 - e^2)a}{1 - e \cos \theta}$$

where e is the eccentricity. For the planet Mercury, $a = 35.0 \times 10^6$ miles and $e = 0.206$.

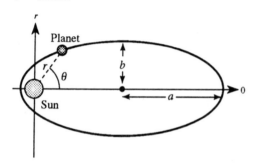

a. Write the polar equation for the path of Mercury and sketch its graph. Find the area of the plane region enclosed by its graph ($A = \pi ab$).

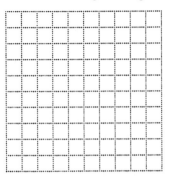

b. Approximate the distance traveled by the planet in one orbit of the sun. Find its average orbital speed in miles per hour if the time for one orbit is 87.969 days.

c. Approximate the area swept out by a ray from the sun to the planet and the distance the planet moves as its position moves from $\theta = 0$ to $\theta = \pi/6$. Use Kepler's Second Law to approximate the average speed of the planet over this interval of time.

d. Approximate the magnitude of a positive angle α such that the area swept out by a ray from the sun to the planet as its position moves from $\theta = \pi - \alpha$ to $\theta = \pi$ equals the area calculated in part **c.** Show these areas on the graph in part **a.**

e. Find the time and distance traveled by the planet over the interval for θ determined in part **d.** What is the average speed of the planet on this interval?

f. Write a short paragraph explaining how the speed of a planet varies in its elliptical orbit.

This worksheet uses a 2D function grapher and matrix operations.

Name _____

Date _____

1. Define a function $\Theta(\mathbf{u}, \mathbf{v})$ on your computer/calculator that yields the angle between the two vectors in degrees. Use the function to find the angle between the given vectors.

    a. $\mathbf{u} = \langle 4, -2 \rangle$
       $\mathbf{v} = \langle -1, 6 \rangle$

    b. $\mathbf{u} = \langle \frac{1}{2}, 4 \rangle$
       $\mathbf{v} = \langle 3, 4 \rangle$

    c. $\mathbf{u} = \langle 6, -2, 1 \rangle$
       $\mathbf{v} = \langle 3, 7, -4 \rangle$

    d. $\mathbf{u} = \langle -4, 3, -2 \rangle$
       $\mathbf{v} = \langle 2, -1, 5 \rangle$

2. Use the function defined in Exercise 1 to find the direction angles of the vector $\langle -2, 4, 3 \rangle$. Verify that the sum of the squares of the cosines of these angles is 1.

3. Define a function Proj(**u**, **v**) on your computer/calculator that yields the projection of **u** onto **v**. Use the function to find the projection of **u** onto **v** for each of the following. Graph the two given vectors and the specified projection.

a. **u** = ⟨4, 5⟩
   v = ⟨8, 3⟩

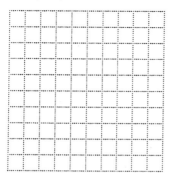

b. **u** = ⟨−3, 2⟩
   v = ⟨8, 3⟩

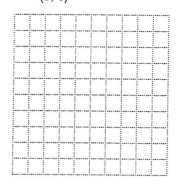

4. Use the function defined in Exercise 3 to find the projection of **u** onto **v**. Graph the two vectors and the specified projection.

a. $\mathbf{u} = \langle 4, 5, 3 \rangle$
  $\mathbf{v} = \langle 6, 1, 0 \rangle$

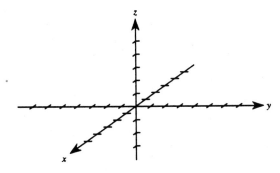

b. $\mathbf{u} = \langle -3, 2, 1 \rangle$
  $\mathbf{v} = \langle 2, 6, -2 \rangle$

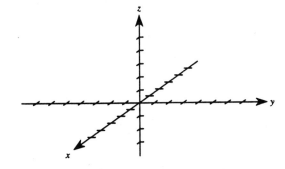

5. Consider the vectors $\mathbf{u} = \langle 4, t \rangle$ and $\mathbf{v} = \langle -3, 5 \rangle$.

    a. Graph the vectors for two distinct values of t. For each value of t use the function defined in Exercise 1 to find the angle between $\mathbf{u}$ and $\mathbf{v}$.

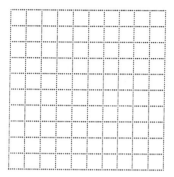

    b. Determine the value of t so that the angle between $\mathbf{u}$ and $\mathbf{v}$ is 180°.

    c. Use the function defined in Exercise 1 to find the angle between $\mathbf{u}$ and $\mathbf{v}$. Note that Θ is a function of t. Use a computer/calculator to graph the function. Identify the horizontal asymptotes of the graph and interpret their meaning in the context of the problem.

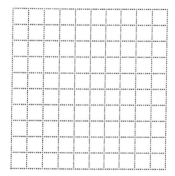

This worksheet uses a 3D function grapher and matrix operations.

Name _____

Date _____

1. Use a computer to find the cross product of the vectors **u** and **v**, and verify that it is orthogonal to both **u** and **v**. Use the computer to graph the given vectors and the cross product.

    a. $\mathbf{u} = \langle 1, 3, 4 \rangle$
       $\mathbf{v} = \langle 4, 1, 1 \rangle$

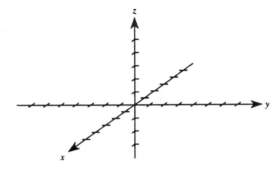

    b. $\mathbf{u} = \langle -2, -1, 0 \rangle$
       $\mathbf{v} = \langle 3, 1, -2 \rangle$

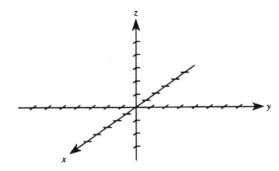

2. Find the area of the triangle with vertices $(-2, -1, -3)$, $(3, -2, 1)$, and $(5, 3, 5)$. ($\frac{1}{2}\|\mathbf{u} \times \mathbf{v}\|$ is the area of the triangle having $\mathbf{u}$ and $\mathbf{v}$ as adjacent sides.)

3. Use a computer/calculator to find the volume of the parallelopiped having $\mathbf{u} = 5\mathbf{i} + 2\mathbf{j} + \mathbf{k}$, $\mathbf{v} = \mathbf{i} + 10\mathbf{j} + 8\mathbf{k}$, and $\mathbf{w} = 2\mathbf{i} - \mathbf{j} + 4\mathbf{k}$, as adjacent edges. Compute the volume by using the triple scalar product.

4. A 5-foot fishing pole is held at a 45° angle with the horizontal when a fish strikes (see figure). As the fish is reeled in, the tension in the line is 10 pounds. Find the torque at the point P as a function of θ, the angle between the line and the pole. Graph this function and determine the maximum torque. Determine the value of θ when this will occur.

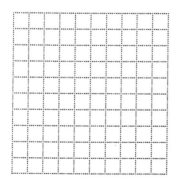

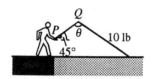

This worksheet uses a 3D grapher.

Name _____

Date _____

1. a. Find a set of parametric equations of the line through the points $(-2, -1 - 1)$ and $(4, 3, 5)$.

b. Use a computer to graph the line through the two points. Rotate the graph in space and sketch the line again.

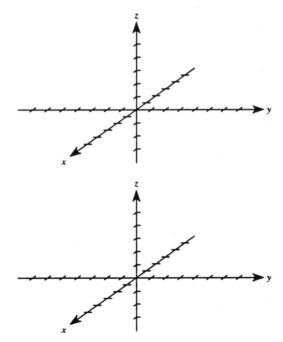

c. Find the distance between the origin and the line. Show the distance on one of the graphs in part **b.**

2. a. Use a computer to graph the lines with parametric equations

$$x = 1 - 2t \qquad \text{and} \qquad x = 3 - s.$$
$$y = 3 + \frac{t}{2} \qquad\qquad y = \frac{5}{2} + 2s$$
$$z = 2 + t \qquad\qquad z = 1 + \frac{s}{2}$$

Rotate the graphs in space to obtain what you think is the best view.

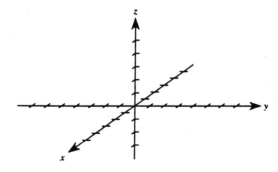

b. Find the point of intersection of the lines and the angle between the lines.

3. a. Find a set of parametric equations of the line of intersection of the planes $3x + 2y + z = 4$ and $x - y - 2z = 2$.

b. Graph the planes and highlight the line of intersection.

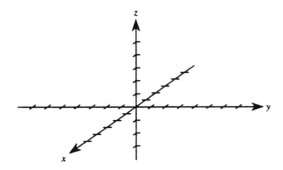

4. A sample of 8 students was selected to study the relationship between math and English placement tests and the cumulative grade point average of a student after the freshman year. The maximum possible score on each placement test was 10. The data from the sample is given in the following table where x and y are the math and English placement scores, respectively, and z is the grade point average.

x	6	7	8	10	3	6	7	7
y	9	6	9	8	3	4	10	7
z	3.5	2.9	3.1	3.9	2.1	2.6	3.2	3.2

A model for this data is given by

$$z = 1.34 + 0.16x + 0.09y.$$

a. Use the model to predict the grade point average for a student with math and English placement test scores of $x = 7$ and $y = 5$.

b. Use a computer to graph the model.

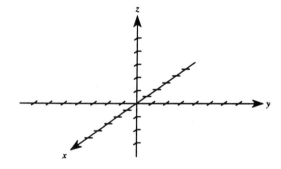

c. In this model, which placement test appears to have the greater effect in predicting the grade point average? Give a reason for your answer.

This worksheet uses a 3D grapher.

Name _____

Date _____

In Exercises 1 and 2, use a computer/calculator to graph the cylinder.

1. $z = 2e^{-x^2/2}$

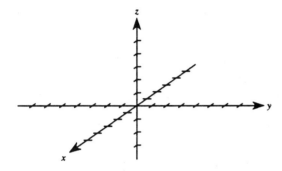

2. $z = \ln y$

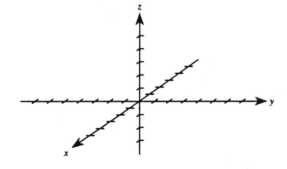

In Exercises 3 and 4 consider the hyperboloid of one sheet given by

$$\frac{x^2}{4} + \frac{y^2}{4} - z^2 = 1.$$

3. Use a computer to graph the surface and rotate it in space so that you are viewing it from the specified point.

a. (10, 10, 10)

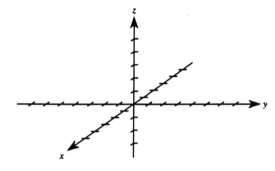

b. (10, 10, 0)

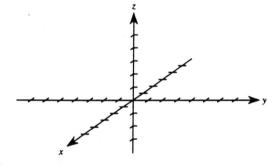

c. (0, 0, 10)

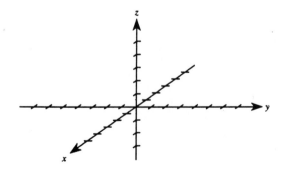

4. Identify the traces that you see when looking at the graphs in parts **b.** and **c.** of Exercise 3.

5. Print two copies of the graph of the hyperbolic paraboloid

$$z = \frac{x^2}{4} - y^2.$$

Rotate the one graph so that you can highlight (by hand) the branches which are parabolas. Select one opening downward and one opening upward. On the second graph highlight a hyperbola.

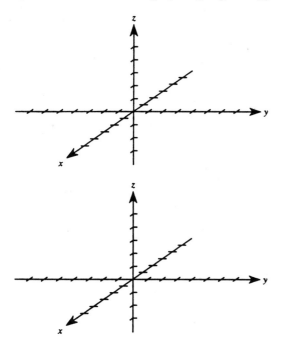

6. The curve $z = \sqrt{y} + 1$, $(0 \le y \le 4)$ in the yz-plane is revolved about the z-axis.

   a. Find an equation for the surface of revolution.

   b. Use a computer to graph the surface of revolution.

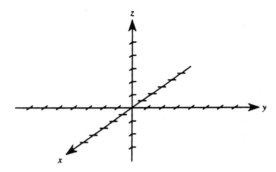

   c. Find the surface area of the surface of revolution.

7. The curve $z = \cos\dfrac{\pi x}{4}$, $(0 \le x \le 2)$ in the xz-plane is revolved about the x-axis.

a. Find an equation of the surface of revolution.

b. Find the volume of the solid bounded by the surface of revolution.

This worksheet uses a 3D grapher.

Name _____

Date _____

In Exercises 1–6, use a computer/calculator to convert the coordinates of a point from one system to another among the rectangular, cylindrical, and spherical coordinate systems. Write the coordinates to three decimal place accuracy.

Rectangular	*Cylindrical*	*Spherical*
1. (2, 4, 8)		
2. (−4, 2, −2)		
3.	$\left(3, \dfrac{\pi}{6}, -1\right)$	
4.	(5, −1.2, 3)	
5.		$\left(10, \dfrac{3\pi}{4}, \dfrac{\pi}{2}\right)$
6.		(3, 0.75, 2)

In Exercises 7 and 8, find an equation in rectangular coordinates for the equation in cylindrical coordinates. Use a computer to graph the equation in cylindrical coordinates.

7. $r = \dfrac{z}{2}$

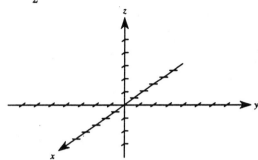

8. $r = 4\cos\theta$

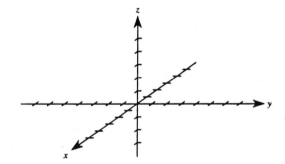

In Exercises 9 and 10, find an equation in rectangular coordinates for the equation in spherical coordinates. Use a computer to graph the equation in spherical coordinates.

9. $\rho = \frac{1}{3} \sin \phi \cos \theta$

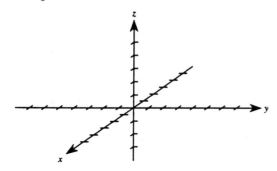

10. $\rho = \frac{1}{2} \csc \phi \cot \phi$

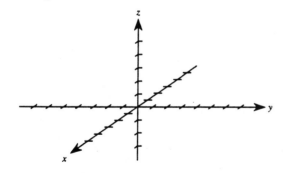

11. A company is considering two designs of a silver napkin holder. One design is given by the cylindrical equation $r = 4 \sin \theta$, $0 \leq \theta \leq \pi$, $-1 \leq z \leq 1$, and the other is modeled by the spherical equation $\rho = 4 \sin \theta \csc \phi$, $0 \leq \theta \leq \pi$, $\pi/3 \leq \phi \leq 2\pi/3$. All distances are measured in centimeters.

   a. Find an equation in rectangular coordinates for each of the models. Are the rectangular equations the same?

b. Use a computer to graph each of the models. Are the graphs the same? Explain any differences you see.

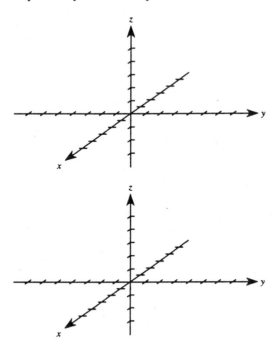

c. Describe the change in the design if the spherical model were used with $\pi/4 \le \phi \le 3\pi/4$.

This worksheet uses a 3D grapher.

Name _____

Date _____

In Exercises 1–4, use a computer to graph the curve represented by the vector-valued function, give its orientation, and identify the curve.

1. $r(t) = (2t - 3)i + (\frac{t}{2} - 2)j - t\,k$

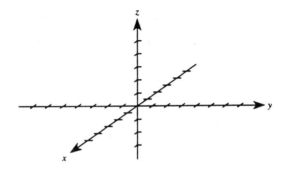

2. $r(t) = (t - 1)i + (t - 1)j - \frac{t^2}{2}\,k$

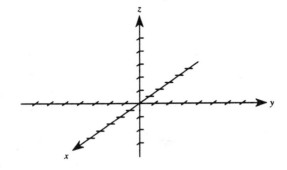

3. $\mathbf{r}(t) = 2\cos t\,\mathbf{i} + 5\sin t\,\mathbf{j} + 2\cos t\,\mathbf{k}$

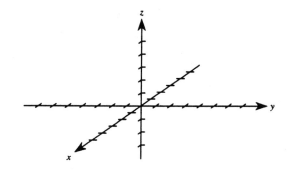

4. $\mathbf{r}(t) = 2\cos t\,\mathbf{i} + 2\sin t\,\mathbf{j} + \dfrac{t}{2}\,\mathbf{k}$

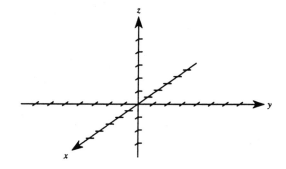

5. Use a computer to graph the vector-valued function

$$\mathbf{r}(t) = 2\cos t\,\mathbf{i} + 2\sin t\,\mathbf{j} - \frac{t}{2}\,\mathbf{k}$$

as viewed from the specified points. In each case identify the curve, and if possible, explain why it is the indicated curve.

a. (10, 10, 10)

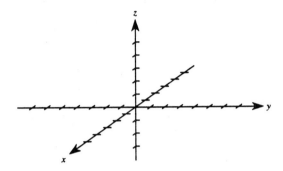

b. (0, 0, 10)

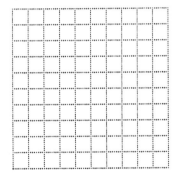

c. $(0, 10, 0)$

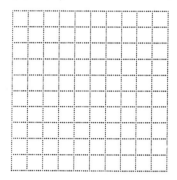

d. $(-10, 0, 0)$

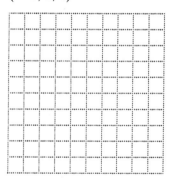

6. Consider the vector-valued function

$$\mathbf{r}(t) = \sqrt{4 - t^2}\cos(2\pi t)\mathbf{i} + \sqrt{4 - t^2}\sin(2\pi t)\mathbf{j} + t\,\mathbf{k}.$$

a. Show that the graph of this function lies on the surface $x^2 + y^2 + z^2 = 4$.

b. Sketch the curve represented by the vector-valued function.

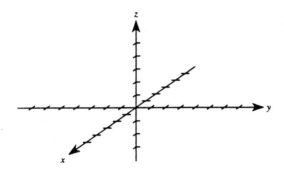

7. a. Use a computer to graph the surfaces $z = \sqrt{x^2 + y^2}$ and $z = \frac{1}{2}(y + 4)$ on the same set of coordinate axes.

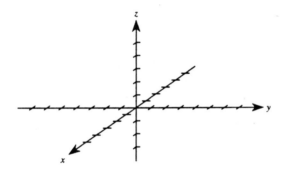

b. Find a set of parametric equations of the curve of intersection of the surfaces in part **a.** Use a computer to sketch the space curve.

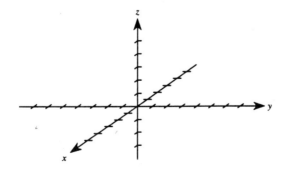

This worksheet uses a symbolic differentiation utility, a symbolic integration utility and a 3D grapher.

Name _____

Date _____

1. Consider the vector-valued function

$$\mathbf{r}(t) = \sqrt{4 - t^2}\cos(2\pi t)\mathbf{i} + \sqrt{4 - t^2}\sin(2\pi t)\mathbf{j} + t\,\mathbf{k}.$$

   a. Use a computer to graph the function and the vectors

$$\mathbf{r}\left(\frac{1}{4}\right), \quad \frac{\mathbf{r}'(\frac{1}{4})}{\|\mathbf{r}'(\frac{1}{4})\|}, \quad \frac{\mathbf{r}''(\frac{1}{4})}{\|\mathbf{r}''(\frac{1}{4})\|}, \quad \text{and} \quad \frac{\mathbf{r}'(\frac{1}{4})}{\|\mathbf{r}'(\frac{1}{4})\|} \times \frac{\mathbf{r}''(\frac{1}{4})}{\|\mathbf{r}''(\frac{1}{4})\|}.$$

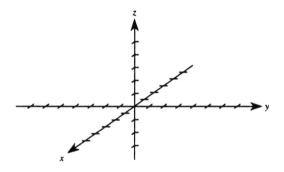

   b. Use a computer to find $\mathbf{r}(t) \cdot \mathbf{r}'(t)$ and give a geometric interpretation of the result.

2. Consider the vector-valued function

$$\mathbf{r}(t) = t\,\mathbf{i} + t^2\,\mathbf{j} + |\sin \pi t|\,\mathbf{k}.$$

a. Use a computer to graph the function and the vectors

$$\mathbf{r}\left(\frac{3}{2}\right), \quad \frac{\mathbf{r}'(\frac{3}{2})}{||\mathbf{r}'(\frac{3}{2})||}, \quad \frac{\mathbf{r}''(\frac{3}{2})}{||\mathbf{r}''(\frac{3}{2})||}, \quad \text{and} \quad \frac{\mathbf{r}'(\frac{3}{2})}{||\mathbf{r}'(\frac{3}{2})||} \times \frac{\mathbf{r}''(\frac{3}{2})}{||\mathbf{r}''(\frac{3}{2})||}.$$

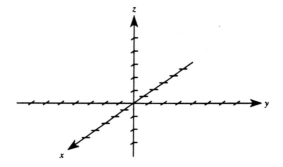

b. Use a computer to graph $\mathbf{r}'(t)$ and use the graph to determine the intervals where $\mathbf{r}'(t)$ is continuous and $\mathbf{r}(t)$ is smooth.

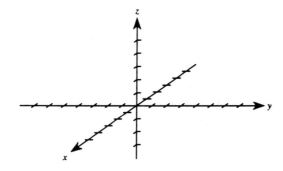

3. a. Find $\mathbf{r}(\theta)$ given that $\mathbf{r}'(\theta) = \left\langle \theta \cos \theta, \theta \sin \theta, \dfrac{1}{2} \right\rangle$ and $\mathbf{r}\left(\dfrac{\pi}{2}\right) = \langle \pi, 0, 1 \rangle$.

b. Use a computer to graph $\mathbf{r}(\theta)$ for $0 \leq \theta \leq 4\pi$.

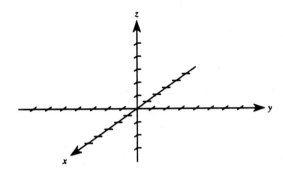

This worksheet uses symbolic differentiation utility and a 3D grapher.

Name _____

Date _____

1. An illustration from the manual for GyroGraphics^{tm} uses the helix given by the vector-valued function

$$\mathbf{r}(t) = t\,\mathbf{i} + \sin t\,\mathbf{j} + \cos t\,\mathbf{k}.$$

   a. Graph the curve and the tangent vector at the point on the curve when $t = \pi$.

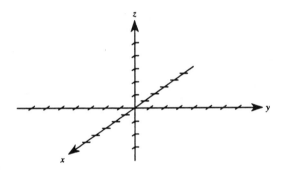

   b. Rotate the graph so that the x-axis is horizontal. Now rotate the graph continuously about the x-axis and watch the tangent vector as it appears to move along the curve. Discuss the changes in slope of the tangent vector in relation to concavity, extrema, and points of inflection.

2. Consider an object moving on the elliptical path given by the vector-valued function $\mathbf{r}(t) = 5\cos t\,\mathbf{i} + 3\sin t\,\mathbf{j}$.

a. Use a computer to find $\mathbf{v}(t)$, $\|\mathbf{v}(t)\|$, and $\mathbf{a}(t)$. Complete the following table by finding the required speed of the object.

t	0	$\dfrac{\pi}{4}$	$\dfrac{\pi}{2}$	$\dfrac{2\pi}{3}$	π
Speed					

b. Use a computer to graph the elliptical path along with the velocity and acceleration vectors at the values of t given in the table in part a.

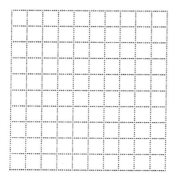

c. Use the results of parts a. and b. to describe the geometric relationship between the velocity and acceleration vectors and the change of speed of the object.

3. An object moves along the space curve given by the vector-valued function

$$r(t) = \frac{1}{2}(t \cos \pi t\, \mathbf{i} + t \sin \pi t\, \mathbf{j} + t\, \mathbf{k}).$$

a. Use a computer to graph the space curve and the unit vectors in the direction of the velocity and acceleration vectors for $t = \frac{1}{2}$ and $t = 3$.

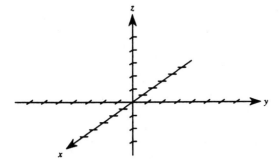

b. Determine if the speed is increasing or decreasing as the object moves up the spiral path. Justify your answer.

c. Express the angle θ in degrees between the velocity and acceleration vectors as a scalar function of t. Find $\lim_{t \to \infty} \theta(t)$.

d. Find a set of parametric equations for the tangent line to the curve when $t = 3$.

This worksheet uses a symbolic differentiation utility and a 3D grapher.

Name _____

Date _____

1. A projectile is launched with an initial velocity of 100 feet per second at a height of 5 feet and at an angle of 30° with the level ground.

    a. Determine the vector-valued function for the path of the projectile. Use a computer to graph the function and determine the maximum height and the range of the projectile.

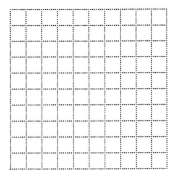

    b. Find the vector-valued functions for the velocity and acceleration of the projectile. Evaluate the two functions for $t = 0.5$, $t = 1.5$, and $t = 3$. Use a computer to sketch these vectors at the proper position along the curve sketched in part **a**. Determine when the speed of the projectile is increasing and when it is decreasing. What is the relationship between the velocity and acceleration vectors in each case?

c. Complete the following table by calculating the speed of the projectile at the specified times.

t	0.5	1.0	1.5	2.0	2.5	3.0
Speed						

d. Use a computer to determine $\mathbf{T}(t)$, $\mathbf{N}(t)$, $a_\mathbf{T}$, and $a_\mathbf{N}$ and verify that

$$\mathbf{a} = a_\mathbf{T}\mathbf{T} + a_\mathbf{N}\mathbf{N}.$$

e. Use a computer to graph the scalar functions $a_\mathbf{T}$ and $a_\mathbf{N}$. How is the speed of the projectile changing when the two graphs have opposite signs?

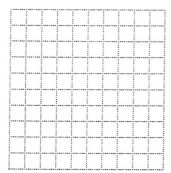

2. Because of a storm, ground controllers instruct the pilot of a plane flying at an altitude of 4 miles to make a 90° turn and climb to a height of 4.2 miles. The model for the path of the plane during this maneuver is

$$\mathbf{r}(t) = \langle 10\cos 10\pi t,\ 10\sin 10\pi t,\ 4 + 8t \rangle, \quad 0 \le t \le \frac{1}{20}$$

where t is time in hours and distance is in miles.

a. Determine the speed of the plane.

b. Use a computer to find the vectors $\mathbf{T}(t)$, $\mathbf{N}(t)$, and $\mathbf{B}(t) = \mathbf{T}(t) \times \mathbf{N}(t)$. Graph the curve and the three unit vectors you just calculated, when $t = \frac{1}{10}$.

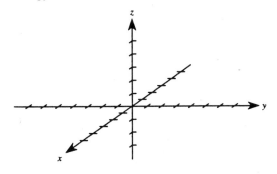

c. Use a computer to calculate $a_{\mathbf{T}}$ and $a_{\mathbf{N}}$. Why is the one 0? Use the computer to verify that

$$\mathbf{a} = a_{\mathbf{T}}\mathbf{T} + a_{\mathbf{N}}\mathbf{N}.$$

d. The vectors **T**, **N**, and **B** found in part **b.** constitute a triad of mutually orthogonal unit vectors moving along the curve. The rate at which these vectors turn is call **torsion**, τ, and is given by

$$\tau(t) = \frac{\mathbf{r}'(t) \cdot (\mathbf{r}''(t) \times \mathbf{r}'''(t))}{||\mathbf{r}'(t) \times \mathbf{r}''(t)||^2}.$$

Use a computer to find the torsion and show that it is constant as the plane flies through this maneuver.

3. Consider the vector-valued function $\mathbf{r}(t) = t\,\mathbf{i} + t^2\,\mathbf{j} + t^3\,\mathbf{k}$. Use the definitions of **B** and τ from Exercise 2 in each of the following.

a. Sketch the curve and the vectors **T**(1), **N**(1), and **B**(1).

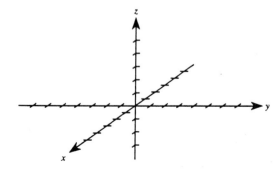

b. Find the torsion $\tau(t)$. When is the torsion maximum? Find $\lim\limits_{t \to \infty} \tau(t)$. Are these answers comparable with the graph in part **a.**? Explain.

This worksheet uses a symbolic differentation utility, a symbolic integration utility and a 3D grapher.

Name _____

Date _____

1. Consider the vector-valued function $\mathbf{r}(t) = \langle t \cos \pi t, \, t \sin \pi t, \, t \rangle$, $0 \leq t \leq 2$.

    a. Use a computer to approximate to 3 decimal places the length of the arc from $t = 0$ to $t = 2$.

    b. Use a computer to find the curvature K as a function of t. Use the function to complete the following table.

t	0	1	2	$\rightarrow \infty$
$K(t)$				

    c. Sketch the space curve. Use the graph and the table in part **b.** to briefly describe how the bending of the curve changes with increasing t.

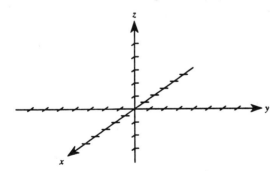

2. The set of centers of curvature of a curve is called the **evolute** of that curve. The evolute of the ellipse $\mathbf{r}(t) = 5\cos t\,\mathbf{i} + 3\sin t\,\mathbf{j}$ is $\mathbf{s}(t) = \frac{16}{5}\cos^3 t\,\mathbf{i} - \frac{16}{3}\sin^3 t\,\mathbf{j}$. Use a computer/calculator to graph the ellipse and its evolute. Then use a compass to draw four circles of curvature to ellipse. Write a short comparison of similar characteristics of the ellipse and the circle of curvature at their point of tangency.

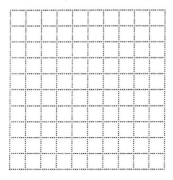

3. The surface of a goblet is formed by revolving the graph of the function

$$y = \frac{x^{8/5}}{4}, \quad 0 \le x \le 5$$

about the y-axis. (The measurements are given in centimeters.)

a. Find the volume of the goblet.

b. Find the curvature of the generating curve and sketch its graph as a function of x. If a spherical object is dropped into the goblet, is it possible for it to touch the bottom? Explain.

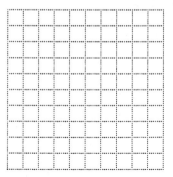

4. Consider the function $f(x) = x^4 - x^2$.

   a. Use a computer to find the curvature K of the curve as a function of x. Use it to find the circle of curvature to the graph of f when $x = 0$, $x = \sqrt{2}/2$, and $x = 1$.

   b. Use a computer to graph the function f and the three circles of curvature in part **b.**

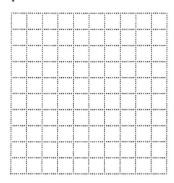

c. Graph the function $K(x)$ and compare it with the graph of $f(x)$. For example, do the extrema of f and K occur at the same critical numbers? Be careful!

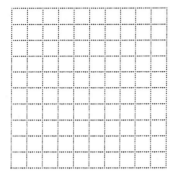

This worksheet uses 2D and 3D function graphers.

Name _____

Date _____

1. Consider the function $f(x, y) = x^3 - 3xy^2$.

   a. Use a computer/calculator to sketch views of the surface from the points $(10, 10, 10)$ and $(-10, -10, 10)$.

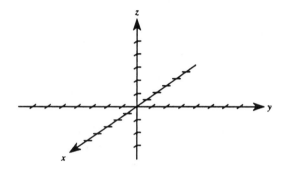

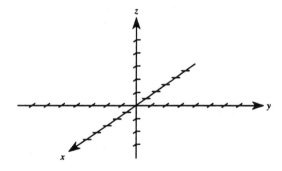

b. Sketch and label the level curves of the surface for
$c = -2$, $c = -1$, $c = 0$, $c = 1$, and $c = 2$.

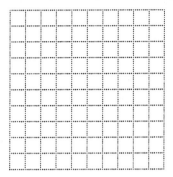

c. Use a computer/calculator to simplify the difference quotient

$$\frac{f(x, y + \Delta y) - f(x, y)}{\Delta y}.$$

2. A retail outlet sells two competitive products, the prices of which are p_1 and p_2. The total revenue over a specified time period is given by

$$R = 500p_1 + 800p_2 + 1.5p_1p_2 - 1.5p_1{}^2 - p_2{}^2.$$

a. Sketch the level curves of the function for $c = \$200,000$, $c = \$300,000$, and $c = \$400,000$.

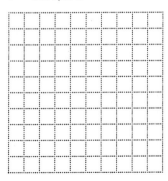

b. Identify the level curves of the graph in part **a**. Shade the region in which the prices can be set and the revenue will range between $300,000 and $400,000. Assuming this model is correct, can the revenue be increased without bound by judicious setting of the prices? Explain.

In Exercises 3 and 4, a. use a computer/calculator to graph the surface given by $f(x, y)$, b. graph selected level curves of the surface, c. determine any points of discontinuity, and find (if possible)

$$\lim_{(x,y)\to(0,0)} f(x, y).$$

3. $f(x, y) = \dfrac{x^2 - y^2}{x^2 + y^2}$

a.

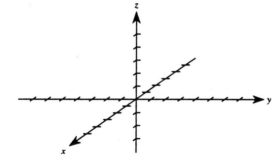

b.

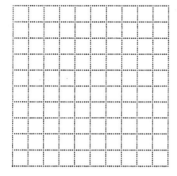

4. $f(x, y) = \dfrac{(x^2 - y^2)^2}{x^2 + y^2}$

a.

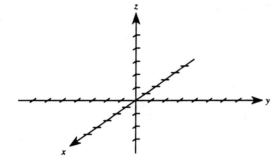

b.

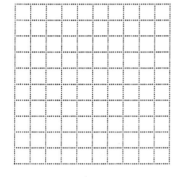

This worksheet uses a symbolic differentiation utility and a 3D grapher.

Name _____

Date _____

1. Consider the function $f(x, y) = \dfrac{(x - y)^2}{x^2 + y^2}$.

    a. Use a computer/calculator to graph the function.

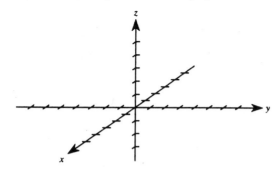

    b. Use a computer/calculator to find all the first and second partial derivatives of the function. Evaluate the first derivatives at the point $(2, -1, \frac{9}{5})$. Identify the traces parallel to the coordinate planes on the graph in part **a** that contain the specified point. Show the tangent lines at the point whose slopes you just calculated.

    c. Identify the paths on the xy-coordinate plane where $f_x(x, y) = 0$ and $f_y(x, y) = 0$. What is the value of the function along each path? Using this information and the graph in part **a**, what is the range of f?

d. Find (if possible) $\displaystyle\lim_{(x,y)\to(0,0)} f(x, y)$.

2. Use a computer/calculator to compute $f_{xyz}(1, \pi/2, 1)$ if $f(x, y, z) = x^2 \sin(xy)e^{xyz}$.

3. The x-coordinate of the centroid of the sector of a circle shown in the accompanying figure is given by

$$\bar{x}(r, \theta) = \frac{2r \sin \theta}{3(\theta - \sin \theta \cos \theta)}.$$

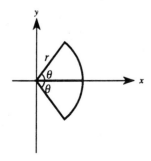

a. Sketch the surface for $0 < r \leq 2$ and $0 < \theta \leq \pi/2$.

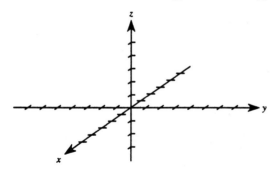

b. Find the first partial derivatives of the function $\bar{x}$ and use the derivatives to complete the following table. Use the entries to describe the rate of change of the location of the x-coordinate of the centroid of the sector for changes in r and θ.

r, θ	$(2, 0.01)$	$\left(2, \dfrac{\pi}{6}\right)$	$\left(2, \dfrac{\pi}{4}\right)$	$\left(2, \dfrac{\pi}{3}\right)$
$\bar{x}_r(r, \theta)$				
$\bar{x}_\theta(r, \theta)$				

This worksheet uses a 2D function grapher and a symbolic differentiation utility.

Name _____

Date _____

1. The height and radius of a cone is measured as 20 meters and 8 meters, respectively. In the process of measuring, errors Δr and Δh are made. If S is the lateral surface area of a cone, complete the table to show the relationship between ΔS and dS for the specified errors.

Δr	Δh	dS	ΔS	$\Delta S - dS$
0.1	0.1			
0.1	−0.1			
0.001	0.002			
−0.0001	0.0002			

2. Given the function $w = x \sin y - ze^{-y}$ where $x = s \cos t$, $y = s/4$, and $z = s \sin t$, find $\partial w/\partial s$ and $\partial w/\partial t$ **a.** by the appropriate Chain Rule and **b.** by converting w to a function of s and t before differentiating.

3. Differentiate $\ln \left(z + \dfrac{y}{x} \right) = 10$ implicitly to find $\dfrac{\partial z}{\partial x}$ and $\dfrac{\partial z}{\partial y}$.

4. A baseball is hit at a height of 2 feet at an angle of 60° with the horizontal and with an initial velocity of 100 feet per second. An outfielder at a distance of 270 feet from the batter catches the ball.

    a. Find a vector-valued function for the path of the ball in terms of the parameter t representing time. Use a computer/calculator to graph the function. At what height was the ball caught and what was its maximum height?

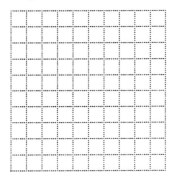

    b. Express the distance d between the ball and the outfielder in terms of x and y and in terms of the parameter t.

    c. Use the results in part b to find the rate of change of d in two ways.

d. Use a computer/calculator to graph the function $d(t)$. At what time is the distance between the ball and the outfielder changing at the slowest rate (i.e., when is $|d'(t)|$ minimum?)? Does it occur at the time the ball reaches its maximum height? Explain.

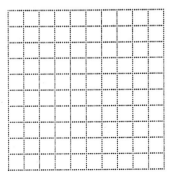

This worksheet uses 2D and 3D function graphers and a symbolic differentiation utility.

Name _____

Date _____

1. Consider the function $f(x, y) = x^2 - y^2$ at the point $(4, -3, 7)$.

   a. Use a computer/calculator to graph the surface.

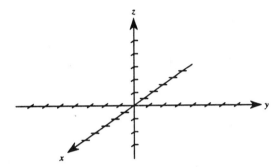

   b. Determine the directional derivative $D_{\mathbf{u}}f(4, -3)$ where $\mathbf{u} = \cos\theta\,\mathbf{i} + \sin\theta\,\mathbf{j}$. The directional derivative will be a function of θ. Use a computer/ calculator to graph this function and determine its zeros and extrema in the interval $[0, 2\pi)$. Interpret each in the context of the given surface. How does the value of the directional derivative change from its maximum value if θ is changed by $90°$ or by $180°$?

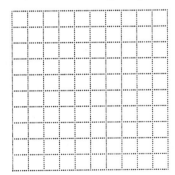

c. Compute $\|\nabla f(4, -3)\|$ and explain its relationship with one of the computations in part **b**.

d. Use a computer/calculator to graph the level curve of the function f at the level $c = 7$. On this graph, sketch the vector $\nabla f(4, -3)$ and state its relationship to the level curve.

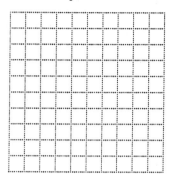

2. The temperature at the point (x, y) on a metal plate is given by

$$T = 400e^{-(x^2+y)/2}, \quad x \geq 0, y \geq 0.$$

a. Use a computer/calculator to graph the temperature distribution function.

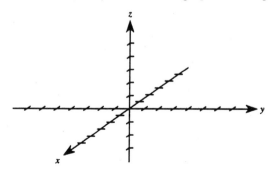

b. Find the direction of greatest increase in heat from the point (3, 5).

c. Find the path followed by a heat-seeking particle placed at the point (3, 5) on the metal plate.

This worksheet uses a symbolic differentiation utility and a 3D function grapher.

Name _____

Date _____

1. a. Find sets of parametric equations for the normal lines and find equations for the tangent planes to the surface

$$f(x, y) = \frac{4xy}{(x^2 + 1)(y^2 + 1)}$$

at the points $(1, 1, 1)$ and $\left(-2, 2, -\frac{16}{25}\right)$.

b. Use a computer/calculator to graph the surface and the normal lines and tangent planes in part **a**. Use the graph and the results of your computation to give a brief description of the behavior of the function at the given points.

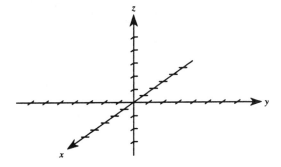

2. Consider the functions $f(x, y) = 6 - x^2 - y^2/4$ and $g(x, y) = 2x + y$.

    a. Find a set of parametric equations of the tangent line to the curve of
    intersection of the surfaces at the point $(1, 2, 4)$ and find the angle between
    the gradient vectors at this point.

    b. Use a computer/calculator to graph the surfaces showing the tangent line
    found in part **a**.

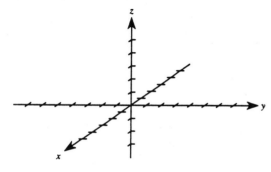

3. Use a computer/calculator to graph the first octant portion of the surfaces given by

$$z = \sqrt{16 - x^2 - y^2 + 2x - 4y} \quad \text{and} \quad z = \frac{\sqrt{2}}{2}\sqrt{1 - 3x^2 + y^2 + 6x + 4y}.$$

These surfaces are orthogonal along the curve of intersection. Find two first octant points on this curve and verify the surfaces are orthogonal at these points.

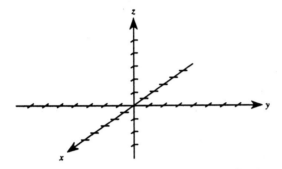

4. Consider the following approximations centered at $(0, 0)$ for a function

$$f(x, y) = \cos x + \sin y.$$

Linear Approximation:
$$P_1(x, y) \approx f(0, 0) + f_x(0, 0)x + f_y(0, 0)y$$

Quadratic Approximation:
$$P_2(x, y) \approx$$
$$f(0, 0) + f_x(0, 0)x + f_y(0, 0)y + \tfrac{1}{2}f_{xx}(0, 0)x^2 + f_{xy}(0, 0)xy + \tfrac{1}{2}f_{yy}(0, 0)y^2$$

[Note that the linear approximation is the tangent plane to the surface at $(0, 0, f(0, 0))$.]

a. Find $P_1(x, y)$.

b. Find $P_2(x, y)$.

c. If $y = 0$ in the quadratic approximation, then you obtain the second degree Taylor polynomial for what function?

d. Complete the following table.

x	y	$f(x, y)$	$P_1(x, y)$	$P_2(x, y)$
0	0			
0	0.1			
0.2	0.1			
0.5	0.3			
1	0.5			

e. Use a computer/calculator to obtain the graph of the surfaces $f(x, y)$, $P_1(x, y)$, and $P_2(x, y)$. How does the accuracy of the approximations change as the distance from $(0,0)$ increases?

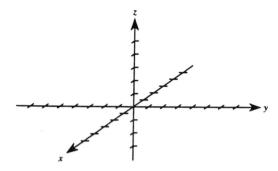

This worksheet uses a symbolic differentiation utility and a 3D function grapher.

Name _____

Date _____

In Exercises 1 and 2, use a computer/calculator to a. graph the function, b. find the critical points and identify any extrema or saddle points by observing the graph, and c. identify any extrema or saddle points by using the Second Partials Test.

1. $f(x, y) = (x^2 + 2y^2)e^{-(x^2+y^2)}$

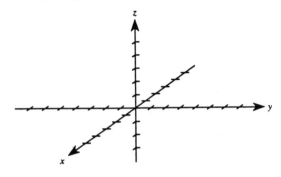

2. $g(x, y) = (-x^2 + 2y^2)e^{-(x^2+y^2)}$

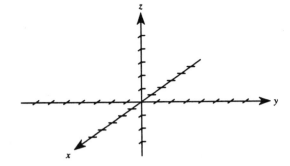

3. Generalize the results of Exercises 1 and 2 for the function

$$f(x, y) = (\alpha x^2 + \beta y^2)e^{-(x^2+y^2)} \text{ where } 0 < |\alpha| \leq \beta.$$

4. Graph the function $f(x, y) = \dfrac{4xy}{(x^2 + 1)(y^2 + 1)}$ and find its absolute extrema over the region R.

a. $R = \{(x, y): \quad 0 \leq x \leq 1, 0 \leq y \leq 1\}$

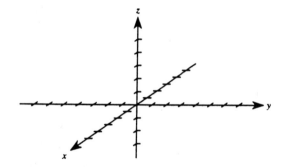

b. $R = \{(x, y): \quad x \geq 0, y \geq 0, x^2 + y^2 \leq 1\}$

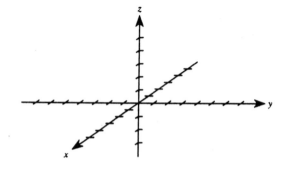

5. The volume of a rectangular open-topped container is 10 cubic meters. The cost of the material for the base and sides is $3 per square meter and $1 per square meter, respectively. The cost for welding each edge is $2 per meter. Find the dimensions of the container of minimum cost.

6. A company has retail outlets located at the points $(-4, 0)$, $(1, 6)$, and $(12, 2)$. Management plans to build a distribution center at the point (x, y) so that the sum of the distances $S(x, y)$ from the center to the outlets is minimum.

   a. Write the expression giving the sum of the distances S. Use a computer/calculator to obtain a graph of the surface. Note that solving $S_x = 0$ and $S_y = 0$ would be very difficult. Therefore, we will approximate the location of the distribution center.

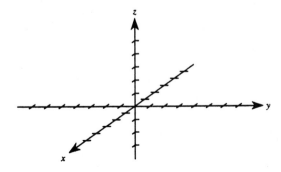

b. If (x_n, y_n) is an estimate of the critical point, then the next approximation can be written in the form

$$(x_{n+1}, y_{n+1}) = (x_n - S_x(x_n, y_n)t, \ y_n - S_y(x_n, y_n)t)$$

where S_x and S_y are the components of ∇S. If these coordinates are substituted into $S(x, y)$, then S becomes a function of the single variable t. Find the value of t which minimizes S. Use this value of t to find the estimate (x_{n+1}, y_{n+1}). Starting with your approximation in part **a**, use a computer/calculator and this algorithm to estimate the location of the distribution center accurate to one decimal place.

14.1 and 14.2 Iterated Integrals, Double Integrals, and Volume

This worksheet uses a 2D function grapher and a symbolic integration utility.

Name _____

Date _____

In Exercises 1 and 2, a. sketch the region of integration in the xy-plane, b. set up the integral for the reverse order of integration, and c. use a computer/calculator to evaluate the integral for both orders of integration.

1. $\displaystyle\int_0^2 \int_{y^3}^{4\sqrt{2y}} (x^2 y - xy^2)\,dx\,dy$

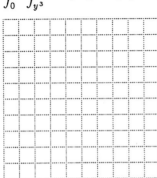

2. $\displaystyle\int_0^2 \int_{\sqrt{4-x^2}}^{4-x^2} \frac{xy}{x^2 + y^2 + 1}\,dy\,dx$

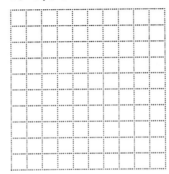

3. a. Set up both orders of the double integrals which yield the volume of the solid bounded by the graphs of the equations $z = 20e^{-x^3/8}$, $y = 0$, $y = x^2$, and $x = 2$.

   b. Use a computer/calculator to attempt to evaluate the integrals in part a. One order is not integrable. Your computer/calculator may have the capability of approximating multiple integrals. If so, use it and compare the result with the value of the integral which is integrable.

4. Consider a continuous function $f(x, y)$ over the rectangular region R with vertices (a, c), (b, c), (a, d) and (b, d) where $a < b$ and $c < d$. Partition the intervals $[a, b]$ and $[c, d]$ into m and n subintervals, respectively, so that the subintervals in a given direction are of equal length. Write a program for your computer/calculator to calculate the sum

$$\sum_{i=1}^{m} \sum_{j=1}^{n} f(x_i, y_i) \Delta x_i \Delta y_j \approx \int_a^b \int_c^d f(x, y)\, dy\, dx$$

where (x_i, y_j) is the center of a representative rectangle in R. Use the program to evaluate each of the following double integrals for the specified values of m and n.

a. $\displaystyle\int_0^2 \int_0^4 20e^{-x^3/8}\, dy\, dx$

$m = 10,\ n = 20$

b. $\displaystyle\int_0^1 \int_3^6 y \cos \sqrt{x}\, dx\, dy$

$m = 10,\ n = 6$

5. In solving a probability problem, it is necessary to find the relationship between the positive constants k and a so that

$$\int_0^\infty \int_0^\infty k e^{-(x+y)/a}\, dy\, dx = 1.$$

Find the relationship.

This worksheet uses 2D and 3D function graphers and a symbolic integration utility.

Name   _____

Date   _____

1. a. It is necessary to determine the volume of the solid bounded by the graphs of the equations

$$z = 25e^{-(x^2+y^2)/4}, \; z = 0, \quad \text{and} \quad x^2 + y^2 = 16.$$

Set up the double integral in rectangular coordinates for finding the required volume. State the difficulty in attempting to evaluate this double integral. Set up and evaluate the double integral in polar coordinates.

    b. Find the diameter of the hole through the solid, centered along the z-axis, which removes one-tenth its volume.

2. Consider the region R in the xy-plane bounded by the graph of the equation

$$(x^2 + y^2)^2 = 9(x^2 - y^2).$$

a. Make the necessary substitutions for x and y to convert the equation to polar form. Use a computer/calculator to solve for r. Graph the polar equation and determine the tangents at the pole.

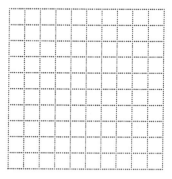

b. Use a double integral to determine the area of the region R. Evaluate the double integral without the aid of a symbolic integration utility.

c. Use a computer/calculator to determine the volume of the solid over the region R and beneath the hemisphere $z = \sqrt{9 - x^2 - y^2}$.

3. The surfaces of a double-lobed cam are modeled by the graphs of the inequalities

$$\frac{1}{4} \le r \le \frac{1}{2}(1 + \cos^2 \theta) \quad \text{and} \quad \frac{-9}{4(x^2 + y^2 + 9)} \le z \le \frac{9}{4(x^2 + y^2 + 9)}$$

where all measurements are in inches.

a. Use a computer to obtain a graph of the cam.

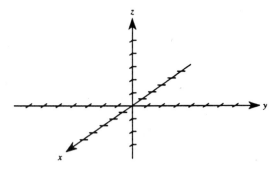

b. Use a computer/calculator to approximate the perimeter of the polar curve

$$r = (1 + \cos^2 \theta)/2.$$

This is the distance a roller must travel as it runs against the cam through one revolution of the cam.

c. Use a computer/calculator to approximate the volume of steel required to make one cam.

This worksheet uses a symbolic integration utility and a 3D function grapher.

Name _____

Date _____

1. A cross-section of a machine part of constant density is shown in the accompanying figure. Determine its moment of inertia and the radius of gyration about the x-axis.

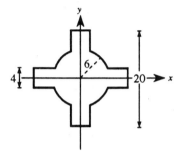

2. Determine the location of the horizontal axis y_a at which the vertical trapezoidal gate in a dam is required to be hinged so that there is no moment causing rotation under the specified loading (see figure). The model for y_a is given by

$$y_a = \bar{y} - \frac{I_{\bar{y}}}{hA}$$

where $\bar{y}$ is the y-coordinate of the centroid of the gate, $I_{\bar{y}}$ is the moment of inertia of the gate about the line $y = \bar{y}$, h is the depth of the centroid below the surface of the water, and A is the area of the gate.

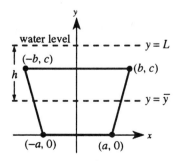

3. Find the area of the surface of the cylinder $f(x, y) = 9 - y^2$ that lies above the triangle bounded by $x = y$, $x = -y$, and $y = 3$.

4. The roof over the stage of an open air theatre of a theme park is modeled by the function

$$f(x, y) = 25 \left[1 + e^{[-(x^2+z^2)/1000]} \cos^2 \left(\frac{x^2 + y^2}{1000} \right) \right]$$

where the stage is a semicircle bounded by $y = \sqrt{50^2 - x^2}$ and $y = 0$.

a. Use a computer/calculator to graph the surface.

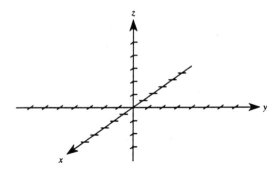

b. Use a computer/calculator to approximate the number of square feet of roofing to cover the surface.

This worksheet uses a symbolic integration utility.

Name _____

Date _____

In Exercises 1 and 2, use a computer/calculator to evaluate the triple integral.

1. $\displaystyle\int_{-1}^{2}\int_{0}^{\sqrt{4-x^2}}\int_{0}^{\sqrt{4-x^2-y^2}} xyz \, dz \, dy \, dx$

2. $\displaystyle\int_{0}^{2\pi}\int_{0}^{a}\int_{0}^{c} \rho^2(\rho^2+b^2) \, dz \, d\rho \, d\theta$

In Exercises 3–8, consider a spherical segment of height h from a sphere of radius a and constant density $\rho(x, y, z) = k$ (see figure).

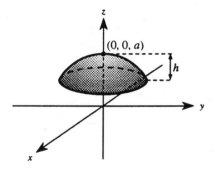

3. Find the volume of the solid.

4. Find the centroid of the solid.

5. Use the result in Exercise 4 to find the centroid of a hemisphere of radius a.

6. Find $\lim_{h \to 0} \bar{z}$.

7. Find I_z.

8. Use the result of Exercise 7 to find I_z for a hemisphere.

9. Find the moment of inertia about the x-axis of the ellipsoid given by

$$\frac{x^2}{a^2} + \frac{y^2}{b^2} + \frac{z^2}{c^2} = 1$$

where $a > b > c > 0$.

This worksheet uses 2D and 3D function graphers and a symbolic integration utility.

Name _____

Date _____

In Exercises 1 and 2, use a computer/calculator to sketch several representative vectors in the vector field.

1. $\mathbf{F}(x, y) = \dfrac{1}{8}(2xy\,\mathbf{i} + x^2\,\mathbf{j})$

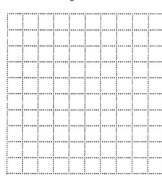

2. $\mathbf{F}(x, y, z) = \dfrac{1}{x^2 + y^2 + z^2}(x\,\mathbf{i} + y\,\mathbf{j} + z\,\mathbf{k})$

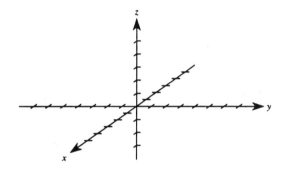

In Exercises 3–6, use a computer/calculator to evaluate the line integral.

3. $\displaystyle\int_C (2x + y)\,ds$

$C : \mathbf{r}(t) = a\cos^3 t\,\mathbf{i} + a\sin^3 t\,\mathbf{j}, \quad 0 \le t \le \pi/2$

4. $\displaystyle\int_C (x^2 + y^2 + z^2)\, ds$

    $C : \mathbf{r}(t) = t\,\mathbf{i} + t^2\,\mathbf{j} + t^{3/2}\,\mathbf{k}, \quad 0 \le t \le 4$

5. $\displaystyle\int_C \mathbf{F} \cdot d\mathbf{r}$

    $\mathbf{F}(x, y) = (2x - y)\,\mathbf{i} + (2y - x)\,\mathbf{j}$

    $C : \mathbf{r}(t) = (2\cos t + 2t\sin t)\,\mathbf{i} + (2\sin t - 2t\cos t)\,\mathbf{j}, \quad 0 \le t \le \pi$

6. $\displaystyle\int_C xy\, dx + (x^2 + y^2)\, dy$

    $C :$ Along the parabolic path $y = x^2$ from $(0, 0)$ to $(2, 4)$ and then back to the origin along the line $y = x$.

7. An object is moved from the point $(-1, 0)$ to the point $(1, 0)$ along the parabolic path $y = c(1 - x^2)$. Find the value of c which minimizes the work if the force field is given by

$$\mathbf{F}(x, y) = 15[(4 - x^2 y)\,\mathbf{i} - xy\,\mathbf{j}].$$

8. The top edge of a solid with vertical sides and resting on the xy-plane is modeled by the vector valued function

$$\mathbf{r}(t) = 3\cos t\,\mathbf{i} + 2\sin t\,\mathbf{j} + [1 + \sin^2(2t)]\,\mathbf{k}.$$

a. Sketch the solid. (Assume rulings across the top and parallel to the yz-coordinate plane are horizontal.)

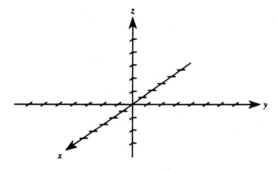

b. Approximate the lateral surface area of the solid.

c. Find (if possible) the volume of the solid.

15.3 and 15.4 Conservative Vector Fields, Independence of Path, & Green's Theorem

This worksheet uses a symbolic differentiation utility.

Name ______________________

Date ______________________

1. Evaluate the integral $\int_C y^2\,dx + 2xy\,dy$ for each of the following.

a. $C: \mathbf{r}(t) = (1+3t)\,\mathbf{i} + (1+t)\,\mathbf{j}, \quad 0 \le t \le 1$

b. $C: \mathbf{r}(t) = t\,\mathbf{i} + \sqrt{t}\,\mathbf{j}, \quad 1 \le t \le 4$

c. Use the Fundamental Theorem of Line Integrals where C is a smooth curve from $(1,\ 1)$ to $(4,\ 2)$.

2. Evaluate the integral $\int_C z \cos(xz)\, dx - z \sin(yz)\, dy + [x \cos(xz) - y \sin(yz)]\, dx$
for each of the following.

a. $C : \mathbf{r}(t) = \dfrac{\pi}{4} t\, \mathbf{i} + \dfrac{\pi}{4} t\, \mathbf{j} + t\, \mathbf{k}, \quad 0 \le t \le 1$

b. Use the Fundamental Theorem of Line Integrals where C is a smooth curve from $(0, 0, 0)$ to $(\pi/4, \pi/4, 1)$.

3. Consider the line integral

$$\int_C y^n\, dx + x^n\, dy$$

where C is the boundary of the region lying between the graphs of $y = \sqrt{a^2 - x^2}$, $(a > 0)$ and $y = 0$. Use a computer/calculator to verify Green's Theorem for integer values of n from 1 to 10 inclusive.

4. Consider the region bounded by the x-axis and one arch of the cycloid with parametric equations $x = a(\theta - \sin\theta)$ and $y = a(1 - \cos\theta)$. Use line integrals to find **a.** the area of the region, and **b.** the centroid of the region.

This worksheet uses a symbolic integration utility and a 3D function grapher.

Name _____

Date _____

1. Consider the surface represented by the vector-valued function

$$\mathbf{r}(u, v) = 3\cos v \cos u\,\mathbf{i} + 3\cos v \sin u\,\mathbf{j} + \sin v\,\mathbf{k}.$$

a. Graph the surface if $0 \le u \le 2\pi$ and $-\dfrac{\pi}{2} \le v \le \dfrac{\pi}{2}$.

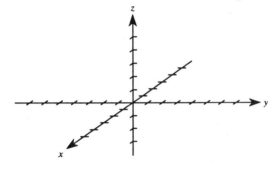

b. Graph the surface if $0 \le u \le 2\pi$ and $\dfrac{\pi}{4} \le v \le \dfrac{\pi}{2}$.

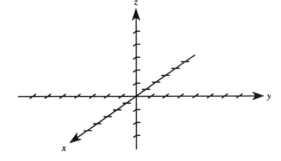

c. Graph the surface if $0 \le u \le \dfrac{\pi}{4}$ and $0 \le v \le \dfrac{\pi}{2}$.

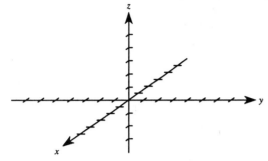

d. Graph and identify the space curve if $0 \le u \le 2\pi$ and $v = \dfrac{\pi}{4}$.

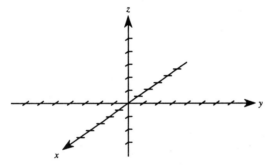

e. Find the area of the surface graphed in part **b**.

f. Find the area of the surface graphed in part **c**.

2 a. Use a computer/calculator to graph the Mobius strip represented by the vector-valued function

$$\mathbf{r}(u,\ v) = (4 - v \sin u) \cos(2u)\,\mathbf{i} + (4 - v \sin u) \sin(2u)\,\mathbf{j} + v \cos u\,\mathbf{k},$$
$$0 \le u \le \pi,\ -1 \le v \le 1.$$

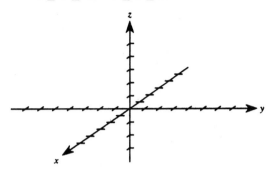

b. Make a Mobius strip by cutting a strip of paper (or find a strip of cash register tape), make a single twist, and paste the ends together. Cut this strip along the space curve represented by $v = 0$ in the graph in part **a**. Describe the result.

3. Use a computer/calculator to approximate

$$\int_S \int f(x,\ y,\ z)\, dS$$

where $f(x,\ y,\ z) = z + 6x^2y^2 - x^2 - y^2$ and the surface S is the paraboloid $z = x^2 + y^2$ with $0 \le z \le 4$.

4. The moment of inertia about the z-axis of a surface lamina of constant density k is given by

$$I_z = k \int_S \int (x^2 + y^2) \, dS.$$

Use a computer/calculator to find the moment of inertia about the z-axis of the lamina in the shape of a torus (e.g. inner tube of a tire) modeled by

$$\mathbf{r}(u, v) = (a + b \cos v) \cos u \, \mathbf{i} + (a + b \cos v) \sin u \, \mathbf{j} + b \sin v \, \mathbf{k}.$$

This worksheet uses a symbolic differentiation utility and a symbolic integration utility.

Name _____

Date _____

1. Let Q be the solid region bounded by the coordinate planes and the plane

$$2x + 4x + z = 8.$$

Verify the Divergence Theorem for $\mathbf{F} = xz\mathbf{i} + 2yz\mathbf{j} + 3xy\mathbf{k}$.

2. Use the Divergence Theorem to evaluate

$$\int_S \int \mathbf{F} \cdot N\,dS$$

and find the outward flux of $\mathbf{F} = xy^2\mathbf{i} + x^2y\mathbf{j} + xz\mathbf{k}$ through the surface of the solid bounded by $z = \sqrt{a^2 - x^2 - y^2}$ and $z = 0$.

3. Verify Stokes's Theorem by evaluating

$$\int_C \mathbf{F} \cdot d\mathbf{r}$$

as a line integral and as a double integral where

$$\mathbf{F} = (z + 2x)\,\mathbf{i} + (x + 2y)\,\mathbf{j} + (y + 2z)\,\mathbf{k}$$

and C is the boundary of the triangle with vertices $(a, 0, 0)$, $(0, a, 0)$, and $(0, 0, a)$.

4. Use Stokes's Theorem to evaluate

$$\int_C \mathbf{F} \cdot d\mathbf{r}$$

as a double integral where $\mathbf{F} = -yz\,\mathbf{i} + xz\,\mathbf{j} + xy\,\mathbf{j}$ and C is the trace of the paraboloid $z = 9 - x^2 - y^2$ in the xy-plane.

This worksheet uses a 2D function grapher and a differential equation solver.

Name _____

Date _____

In Exercises 1–4, use a computer/calculator to a. sketch the direction field of the differential equation, b. find particular solutions of the differential equation passing through the given points, and c. sketch the graphs of the particular solution on the direction field.

1. $y' = \dfrac{1 + y^2}{1 + x^2}$

Points: $(1,\,2),\ (1,\,0)$

2. $y' = \dfrac{xy}{x - 3}$

Points: $(0,\,1),\ (0,\,-1)$

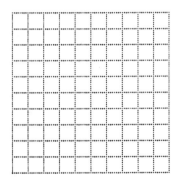

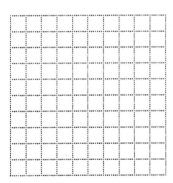

3. $(5x - y)\,dx + (5y - x)\,dy = 0$

Points: $(-1, 1)$, $(-1, 0)$

4. $y' = \dfrac{x^2 + y^2}{xy}$

Points: $(1, 0)$, $(2, 4)$

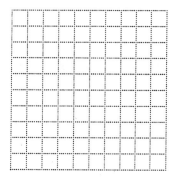

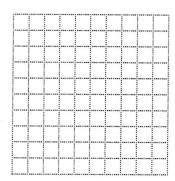

5. The rate of increase in the population P of elk in a game preserve varies jointly as P and $300 - P$ where 300 is the estimated carrying capacity of the preserve. The independent variable is time t measured in years.

    a. Write and solve the differential equation for the population model if $P = 50$ when $t = 0$ and $P = 75$ when $t = 1$.

b. Use a computer/calculator to graph the direction field of the differential equation and the solution of the differential equation. At what time is the population increasing most rapidly?

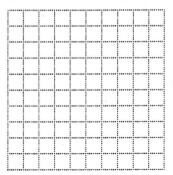

c. If 400 elk had been initially placed in the preserve, use the direction field to describe the change in the population over time.

6. Use a computer/calculator to find the orthogonal trajectories of the family of curves given by $y^2(C - x) = x^3$. Sketch the graphs of at least three members of each family of curves. (*Hint:* It is helpful to convert the orthogonal family to polar coordinates before attempting the sketches.)

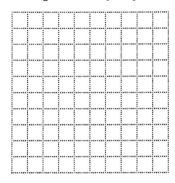

This worksheet uses a 2D function grapher and a differential equation solver.

Name _____

Date _____

In Exercises 1–4, use a computer/calculator to a. sketch the direction field of the differential equation, b. find particular solutions of the differential equation passing through the given points, and c. sketch the graphs of the particular solution on the direction field.

1. $\dfrac{dy}{dx} - \dfrac{1}{x}y = x^2$

   Points: $(-2, 4)$, $(2, 8)$

2. $\dfrac{dy}{dx} + 2xy = x^3$

   Points: $\left(0, \tfrac{7}{2}\right)$, $\left(0, -\tfrac{1}{2}\right)$

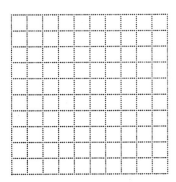

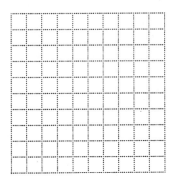

3. $\dfrac{dy}{dx} + \cot xy = x$

Points: $(1, 1)$, $(3, -1)$

4. $\dfrac{dy}{dx} + 2xy = xy^2$

Points: $(0, 3)$, $(0, 1)$

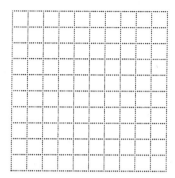

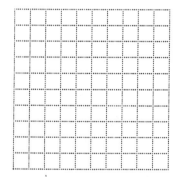

In Exercises 5–8, consider the differential equation $y' + 0.5y = \sin x$ with the initial condition $y(0) = 1$ and $0 \le x \le 5$.

5. Use a computer/calculator to find the particular solution of the differential equation and sketch the graph of the solution over the specified interval.

6. Consider the differential equation $y' = F(x, y)$ with the initial condition $y(x_0) = y_0$. At any point (x_k, y_k) in the domain of F, $F(x_k, y_k)$ yields the slope of the solution at that point. The Euler Method gives a discrete set of estimates of the y values of a solution of the differential equation using the iterative formula

$$y_{k+1} = y_k + F(x_k, y_k)\Delta x$$

where $\Delta x = x_{x+1} - x_k$. In each of the following, use Euler's Method on a computer/calculator to complete the table of approximate solutions to the differential equation.

a.

x_k	0	1	2	3	4	5
y_k						

b.

x_k	0	0.5	1	1.5	2	2.5	3	3.5	4	4.5	5
y_k											

7. Plot the points from each table in Exercise 6 on the graph of the solution to the differential equation. Connect the points from a given table with straight line segments. Use a computer/calculator to repeat the process if $\Delta x = 0.2$.

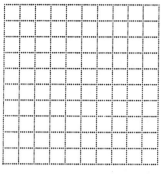 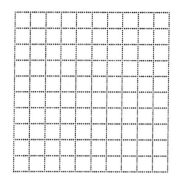

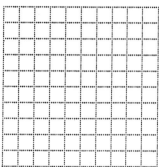

8. Write a short paragraph describing the general idea of how the Euler Method works and how decreasing the magnitude of Δx affects the accuracy of the method.

*This worksheet uses a 2D function grapher
and a differential equation solver.*

Name _____

Date _____

In Exercises 1–4, use a computer/calculator to find and graph
the particular solution of the differential equation satisfying the
boundary conditions.

1. $y'' + 2y' - 3y = 0$

$y(0) = 2, \; y'(0) = 0$

2. $y'' + 2y' + 5y = 0$

$y(1) = 4, \; y(2) = 0$

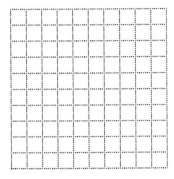

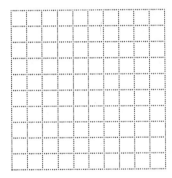

3. $y'' - y' - 2y = 1 + xe^{-x}$

  $y(0) = 1,\ y'(0) = 3$

4. $y'' + 4y' + 4y = \dfrac{e^{-2x}}{x}$

  $y(0) = 0,\ y(1) = 2$

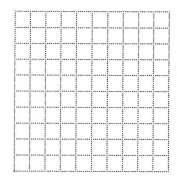

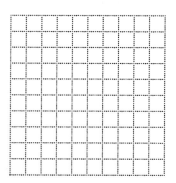

The differential equation

$$\frac{w}{g}y''(t) + by'(t) + ky(t) = \frac{w}{g}F(t)$$

models the oscillating motion of an object on the end of a spring. In the equation, y is the displacement from the equilibrium (positive direction is downward) measured in feet, and t is time in seconds (see figure). The constant w is the weight of the object, g is the acceleration due to gravity, b measures the magnitude of the resistance to the motion, k is the spring constant from Hooke's Law, and $F(t)$ is the acceleration imposed on the system.

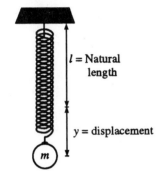

Spring Displacement

In Exercises 5–8, use a computer/calculator to find and graph the particular solution of the differential equation

$$\frac{8}{32}y'' + by' + ky = \frac{8}{32}F(t), \quad y(0) = \frac{1}{2}, \ y'(0) = 0$$

for a given b, k, and $F(t)$.

5. $b = 0$, $k = 1$, $F(t) = 24 \sin \pi t$

6. $b = 0$, $k = 2$, $F(t) = 24 \sin(2\sqrt{2}t)$

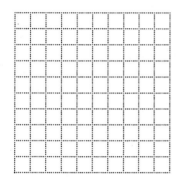

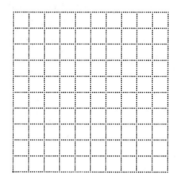

7. $b = 0.1$, $k = 2$, $F(t) = 0$

8. $b = 1$, $k = 2$, $F(t) = 0$

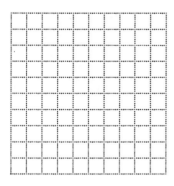

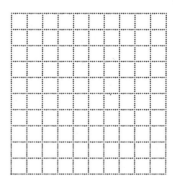

9. **a.** Describe the effect of increasing the resistance to motion, b.

    b. How do you think the motion of the object would change if a stiffer (increased k) spring were used? Explain.

    c. Matching of the input and natural frequencies of a system is known as **resonance**. In which exercise did this occur and what was the result?